The Institute of Biology's
Studies in Biology no. 131

The Evolution of Eukaryotic Cells

Michael Tribe
B.Sc., Ph.D., F.I.Biol.
Lecturer in Biology, University of Sussex

Andrew Morgan
B.Sc., D.Phil.,
Research Fellow, University of Sussex

Peter Whittaker
B.Sc., Ph.D., F.I.Biol.
Professor of Biology, St. Patrick's College,
Maynooth, Ireland

Edward Arnold

© M. A. Tribe, A. J. Morgan and P. A. Whittaker, 1981

First published 1981
by Edward Arnold (Publishers) Limited
41 Bedford Square, London WC1 3DQ

British Library Cataloguing in Publication Data

Tribe, Michael
    The evolution of eukaryotic cells. – (Studies
    in Biology/The Institute of Biology, ISSN 0537–
    9024; no. 131)
    1. Eukaryotic cells   2. Evolution
    I. Title   II. Morgan, Andrew   III. Whittaker,
    Peter *1939–*   IV. Series
    574.87   QH581.2
    ISBN 0–7131–2821–6

Photo Typeset by Macmillan India Ltd. Bangalore

Printed and bound in Great Britain
at The Camelot Press Ltd, Southampton

General Preface to the Series

Because it is no longer possible for one textbook to cover the whole field of biology while remaining sufficiently up to date, the Institute of Biology proposed this series so that teachers and students can learn about significant developments. The enthusiastic acceptance of 'Studies in Biology' shows that the books are providing authoritative views of biological topics.

The features of the series include the attention given to methods, the selected list of books for further reading and, wherever possible, suggestions for practical work.

Readers' comments will be welcomed by the Education Officer of the Institute.

1981   Institute of Biology
                                                        41 Queen's Gate
                                                        London SW7 5HU

Preface

Most of the subjects in this series of monographs emanate from sound observational and experimental evidence, or at least generate hypotheses that are capable of being tested fairly easily in the field or laboratory. The subject matter of this book is concerned with a highly speculative, yet extremely fascinating problem; the evolution of eukaryotic cells. The subject abounds with theories and it is our aim to review and appraise them; but it is much more difficult to collect data or provide clear-cut experimental evidence to confirm any one of these theories with assurance. So we might call it a study based on informed speculation. In such a situation, careful observation from many sources of direct and indirect evidence, coupled with retrospective deduction, are all important in solving difficult questions. Fortunately too, as new physical and chemical techniques become available with the advancement of science and technology, many of these can be applied to difficult problems which hitherto defied solution.

We hope therefore that readers, particularly undergraduates, sixth formers and teachers will find the subject matter both stimulating and thought-provoking. The triple authorship reflects the many interesting discussions that the three of us had on this subject over several years, whilst at the University of Sussex. It is a sequel to an earlier book in this Series *Chloroplasts and Mitochondria*.

Brighton and Maynooth, 1981   M.A.T., A.J.M. and P.A.W.

Contents

1 Introduction

1.1 The problem

Today biologists distinguish between two forms of cellular organization: on the one hand prokaryotic cells (literally 'before a nucleus') and on the other eukaryotic cells (literally 'true nucleus'). Amongst the prokaryotes are to be found all forms of bacteria – eubacteria, spirochaetes, myxobacteria and rickettsiae – all forms of primitive 'fungal-like' bacteria such as streptomyces and mycobacteria, the mycoplasmas, and finally all forms of blue-green algae, better referred to as blue-green bacteria or cyanobacteria. Amongst the eukaryotes are found all animal cells, all green plant cells including algae (but not cyanobacteria), all 'higher' fungi (ascomycetes, basidiomycetes, etc.), and all protozoans. The only other living organisms that do not fall into either of these two categories are the viruses. Viruses are obligate cellular parasites, which are not organized on a cellular plan and can only reproduce within their host cell. These organisms will not be considered further in this book.

For many years, the classical view regarding the evolution of cell types was that all had evolved from a primitive ancestor by gradual accumulation of favourable mutations fostered by natural selection. A major distinction was then made between plant cells, with typically autotrophic nutrition and cellulose cell walls; and animal cells with their heterotrophic nutrition (TRIBE and WHITTAKER, 1981). Indeed, one might argue that the situation in many of our older universities, in which separate departments of botany and zoology were established, engendered not only the dichotomy of interests, but also the earlier distinction between the two cell types, despite the difficulty in deciding whether organisms such as *Euglena* were plant or animal.

However, with technological improvements in light and electron microscopy during the 1950s and early 1960s, more came to be known about the fine structure of cells. It soon became clear that the differences between plant and animal cells were not as great as the fundamental discontinuity that exists between prokaryotic and eukaryotic cells (see STANIER *et al.*, 1970).

1.2 Differences in the cellular organization of prokaryotes and eukaryotes

Examination of prokaryotic and eukaryotic cells reveals that there are numerous and fundamental differences between the two forms of

Table 1 Comparisons between prokaryotic and eukaryotic cells.

Feature	Prokaryotes	Eukaryotes
1 Size	Usually 1–10 μm (diameter)	Usually between 10–100 μm (sometimes > 100)
2 Nucleus	Absent: only areas (nucleoids) where DNA and enzymes necessary for DNA and RNA synthesis are located	Present, with distinct bounding membranes perforated by nuclear pores
3 Nucleolus	Absent	One (or more) present in each nucleus
4 DNA	Simple duplex not associated with histones (i.e. basic proteins)	DNA always in combination with histone proteins
5 Linkage group	Single and circular	Linear and multiple (i.e. chromosomes)
6 Cell division	By fission (mitosis and meiosis absent)	By mitosis or meiosis
7 Spindle	Absent	Present temporarily during mitosis and meiosis
8 Sexual system	Unidirectional transfer of genes from donor to recipient	Complete nuclear fusion between gametes with equal contributions from both genome
9 Cell wall	Present, but chemically different in many respects from eukaryotes (e.g. presence of muramic acid)	Present in plant cells, but never contain muramic acid
10 Internal membranes	Usually simple and often transient, if present at all	Complex compartmentation into endoplasmic reticulum, Golgi bodies, lysosomes, etc.
11 Ribosomes	70 S* with subunits (30 S + 50 S)	80 S with subunits (60 S + 40 S)
12 Photosynthesis	Simple chromatophores	Complex chloroplasts (membrane-bound organelles)
13 Respiration	Anaerobic, microaerophilic and aerobic forms found	Virtually all forms are aerobic, though a few are facultatively anaerobic (e.g. yeasts); and uniquely the trichomonads are obligate anaerobes
14 Electron transport system & ATP synthesis	Localized on the cell membrane	Found on the inner membrane of special membrane bound organelles: mitochondria – oxidative phosphorylation; chloroplasts – photophosphorylation
15 Nutrition	Heterotrophic absorption by diffusion control processes: some photo-autotrophy and some chemo-autotrophy also	Heterotrophic by absorption, ingestion: also autotrophy (photosynthesis)
16 Motility	Simple flagella, if present	Complex cilia and flagella, if present (based on a 9 outer and 2 central microtubular structure in cross section)
17 Tissue formation	Absent (rarely multicellular)	Present in most multicellular organisms
18 Approximate origin	3.5×10^9 years ago	1.5×10^9 years ago

*S – Svedberg unit or sedimentation coefficient.

cellular organization. These differences are summarized in Table 1 and many are highlighted again in Figs 1–1 to 1–5.

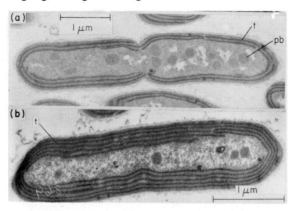

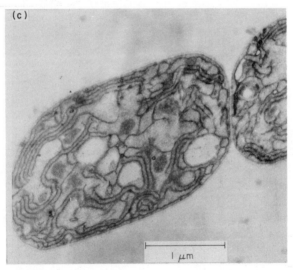

Fig. 1–1 Prokaryotic cells of cyanobacteria (**a**) and (**b**) *Anacystis nidulans* and (**c**) *Anabaena cylindrica*. (**a**) 2-3 thylakoids (t) restricted to the cell periphery; pb, polyhedral body. (**b**) 4-5 thylakoids at periphery with clearly defined central region. (**c**) Thylakoids generally peripheral but also permeating all aspects of the cell. ((a) and (b) Courtesy of Drs N. G. Carr and B. A. Whitton. In *Biology of Blue-green Algae*, Botanical Monographs 9, Blackwell, Oxford. (c) Courtesy of Dr L. De Vasconcelos and Prof. P. Fay, Westfield College, unpublished.)

In Fig. 1–1, cells of two different cyanobacteria, *Anacystis* and *Anabaena* are shown, and in Fig. 1–2 cells of the bacterium *Escherichia*

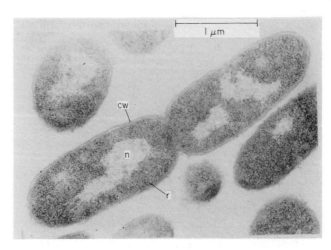

Fig. 1–2 Prokaryotic cells of the bacterium *Escherichia coli* during cell division by simple fission. n, nucleoid; cw, cell wall; r, ribosomes. (Courtesy of Dr A. Ryter, Institut Pasteur, Paris.)

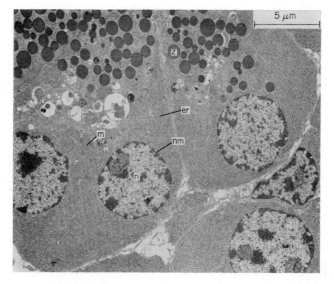

Fig. 1–3 A group of eukaryotic acinar cells from rat pancreas showing the complex arrangement of intracellular membranes and organelles; m, mitochondria; n, nucleus; nm, nuclear membrane; er, rough endoplasmic reticulum; z, zymogen granules. (Courtesy of Dr G. Bullock, CIBA Laboratories, Horsham.)

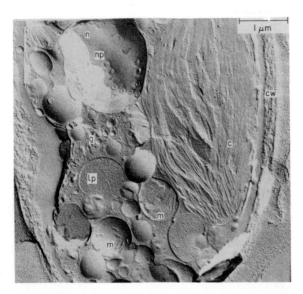

Fig. 1–4 Freeze-etched preparation of a single-celled green alga (eukaryote), *Oocystis marssonii*. n, nucleus; np, nuclear pores; m, mitochondria; g, Golgi body; c, chloroplast; lp, lipid vesicle; cw, cell wall. (Courtesy of Prof. H. C. Aldrich, University of Florida.)

coli are seen dividing by simple fission. *Anacystis, Anabaena* and *Escherichia coli* are all typical prokaryotic cells.

By contrast Fig. 1–3 shows a group of animal cells (acinar cells of rat pancreas) in which the complex organization of internal membranes gives rise to recognizable organelles that typify eukaryotic cells. Figure 1–4 shows another eukaryotic cell: this green algal cell has a single prominent chloroplast, a nucleus, several mitochondria, Golgi bodies, and membrane-bound vesicles containing lipids. Finally, Fig. 1–5 shows a group of plant cells from the root tip of a wheat seedling. Some of these cells are in the process of mitotic division, so that condensed forms of linear chromosomes attached to microtubules of the spindle apparatus, are clearly evident.

The ten-fold difference in size (as can be seen from the scales on these pictures), together with the presence of a prominent nucleus and membrane-bound organelles such as chloroplasts and mitochondria are immediately recognizable and unique features of eukaryotic cells.

1.3 The reasons for thinking that eukaryotes evolved from prokaryotes

Despite the numerous and fundamental differences in their basic

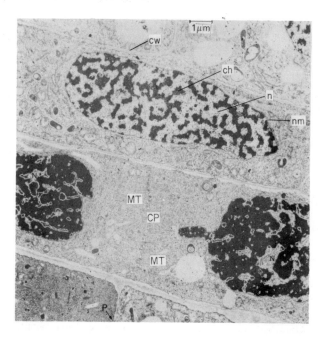

Fig. 1–5 Mitotic cell division in eukaryotic plant cells from wheat coleoptile MT, microtubules; ch, chromatin; cw, cell wall; n, nucleus; nm, nuclear membrane; CP, cell plate; P, plasmodesmata. (Courtesy of Dr. J. D. Pickett-Heaps, University of Colorado.)

cellular design, prokaryotes and eukaryotes have not evolved by totally separate routes; and there are two main reasons for supposing this.

1) The earliest prokaryotes appeared about 3.5×10^9 years ago, whereas the first eukaryotes appeared much later around 1.5×10^9 years ago in the Upper Pre-Cambrian era.

2) A comparison of the basic biochemistry and genetics of all living cells indicates that eukaryotes were derived from prokaryotes. For example, the six most common chemical elements occurring in all living cells are carbon, hydrogen, oxygen, nitrogen, phosphorus and sulphur. Furthermore, the basic hereditary material DNA (deoxyribose nucleic acid) is common to all cells. This semi-conservatively, self-replicating molecule, is always responsible for transcribing three forms of RNA (ribose nucleic acid) – namely messenger RNA, transfer or soluble RNA and ribosomal RNA (abbreviated as mRNA, tRNA and rRNA respectively). In turn these molecules are collaboratively responsible for translating genetic messages, by a triplet code (see p. 51) from DNA into polypeptides and proteins. So ubiquitous is this mechanism of self-replication, transcription and translation amongst living cells, that it has been described as the 'Central Dogma' of biology (Fig. 1–6). The

proteins produced by this process, not only provide much of the structure of all living cells, but in the form of enzymes are typically the catalytic agents responsible for all aspects of cellular metabolism. Again, at the periphery of all cells, selectively permeable membranes are found. These membranes always contain phospholipids arranged as a bimolecular layer associated with proteins (LOCKWOOD, 1979) even though the ratio of lipid: protein and the chemical species of lipids and proteins present, may differ from cell to cell. Finally, any form of life requires a source of energy to maintain it, whether this is achieved autotrophically or heterotrophically. In both cases, electrons and protons, sometimes together, sometimes separately, are shuttled around cells in conjunction with a carbon skeleton. These oxidation-reduction reactions allow energy to be captured (ultimately from sunlight) and transformed within all living cells to perform useful work. The most common energy 'currency' used by all living cells for their various activities is ATP (adenosine triphosphate), which is primarily synthesized by linking electron transport to the phosphorylation of ADP (adenosine diphosphate). Electron transport and ATP synthesis (see Table 1) in aerobic bacteria are carried out within the limiting cell membrane, or by chromophore membranes in the case of blue-green bacteria; whereas this function is performed within the internal membranes of specialized organelles – chloroplasts and mitochondria – in eukaryotic cells.

There seems little doubt therefore that eukaryotes evolved from prokaryotes, but the question is how.

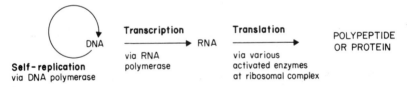

Fig. 1–6 'The Central Dogma'.

1.4   The historical background to cellular evolution

1.4.1   From reducing to oxidizing environment

If it is assumed that the sun, planets, meteors and other aspects of the solar system were all derived from the same primordial dust cloud, then estimates of the age of the earth, based on radioactive dating of meteorites, suggest that it was formed about 4.6×10^9 years ago.

Palaeontological evidence reveals that primitive bacteria-like fossils (prokaryotes) were present in the earth's most ancient rocks, estimated to be between 3.2 to 3.4×10^9 years old. It is likely therefore that the earliest forms of life began somewhere between 3.5 and 4.0×10^9 years ago.

How the first cells originated is beyond the scope of this book, but interested readers are referred to the fascinating work by Miller, Urey and Oparin, reviewed recently by DICKERSON (1978).

Amazingly, the unlikely happening, that of life appearing on earth, not only took place, but by the standards of evolutionary time scales, took place quite rapidly. Figure 1–7 briefly summarizes some of the likely evolutionary pathways taken by prokaryotic cells. What we can be fairly certain about is that the atmosphere of the primitive earth was a reducing one, i.e. it almost certainly contained appreciable amounts of water, abundant nitrogen, some carbon dioxide and probably hydrogen gas, methane and ammonia dissolved in the oceans. As a result, the earliest cells would have respired anaerobically by fermentation. A little later, the ability of some prokaryotes to fix atmospheric nitrogen, and others to reduce nitrates and nitrites was developed. With still other forms evolving the ability to 'oxidize' hydrogen sulphide, the beginning of adaptive radiation in the prokaryote world came about. During this period, which must have lasted about 1.0 to 1.5×10^9 years, crucial porphyrin and isoprenoid macromolecules that we still recognize today, such as cytochromes, chlorophylls and carotenoids, were used more extensively alongside an increasing array of enzymes.

However, the most dramatic change in the earth's atmosphere began about 2.5 to 3.0×10^9 years ago, when there was an accumulation of free oxygen. It is generally believed that the initial origin of this oxygen was from certain blue-green bacteria which had evolved an oxygen-releasing photosystem (PSII) to capture energy from sunlight and transform it into ATP and chemical reducing power by the photolysis (splitting) of water (see Fig. 1–8).

In blue-green bacteria and eukaryote photosynthesizers, PSII operates in series with photosystem I (PSI), which is homologous with the electron transport pathway of anaerobic photosynthetic bacteria. The latter, however, do not possess PSII and do not release oxygen as a by-product of photolysis. Instead, anaerobic photosynthetic bacteria derive their electrons from substances other than water. For example, the purple sulphur bacteria use hydrogen sulphide (H_2S) as a photosynthetic electron donor, by oxidizing the substrate to free sulphur.

The idea that the acquisition of PSII initiated the change in the atmosphere from reducing to oxidizing sounds plausible, but there have been objections raised against it. For instance, oxidized bands of iron dated at 3.8×10^9 years old have been discovered in Greenland, but no oxygenic microfossils of that age have ever been found. Secondly, it seems unlikely that PSII could have evolved under reducing conditions because in such an environment modern blue-green bacteria will not choose water as an electron donor, if other electron donors for PSI are

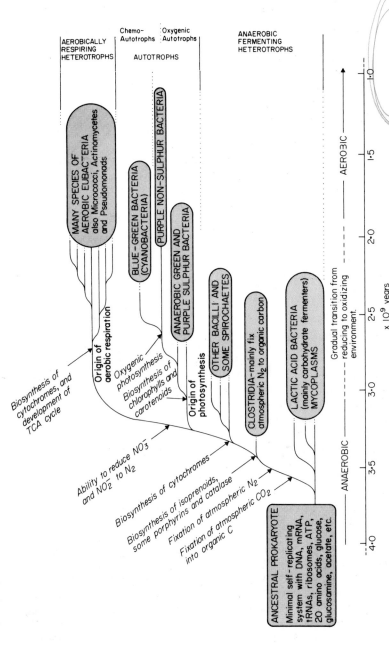

Fig. 1-7 Postulated evolutionary pathways taken by prokaryotic cells. (Simplified and adapted after MARGULIS, 1970.)

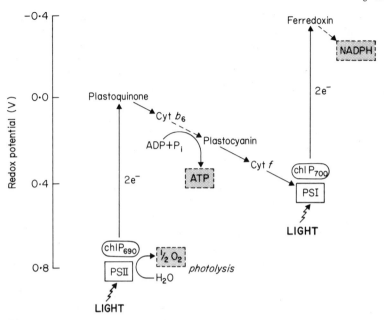

Fig. 1–8 Scheme illustrating photolysis of water and non-cyclic photophosphorylation.

available. Thus it would have been necessary to remove the alternative reducing substances (e.g. H_2S) to PSI before the selective pressures were significant enough to evoke the evolutionary development of PSII. This would have required oxidizing conditions prior to the appearance of oxygen-eliminating photosynthesis. To explain these and other findings, it has been suggested that the *initial* increase in free oxygen was brought about by the photodissociation of water vapour in the atmosphere by ultraviolet light and not by a biotic process. Nevertheless, whatever the cause of the initial appearance of atmospheric oxygen, there is little doubt that the eventual global increase in free oxygen leading to the conditions prevailing today was the result of oxygenic photosynthesis.

Once the earth's atmosphere had become oxidizing, then some of the oxygen was converted to ozone in the upper atmosphere and this ozone layer in turn provided the earth's surface with a protective shield against the energetic ultraviolet light. Although ultraviolet light may have been of considerable importance as a source of energy for biochemical synthesis in the reducing atmosphere, we now know that it has mutagenic or even lethal effects on many present-day bacteria, so that early life forms must have had efficient systems for repairing DNA.

1.4.2 The effect of an oxidizing environment on living cells

The advent of an oxidizing atmosphere, however, had important repercussions for many existing prokaryotes, since prolonged exposure of obligate anaerobes to oxygen is lethal. Consequently, there were three alternatives open to obligate anaerobes: either they rapidly became extinct, or they occupied niches that were still strictly anaerobic, or they adapted to increasingly aerobic conditions. How such cells adapted to the changing conditions is difficult to ascertain, but a number of alternative mechanisms have been proposed. Some organisms almost certainly became facultative aerobes/anaerobes like present day yeasts (eukaryotes) and certain bacteria. Others became tolerant to (and perhaps even utilized) very low concentrations of oxygen, characteristic of present-day microaerophilic bacteria. Nevertheless, the typical aerobic pathway as we know it today (Fig. 1–9) may not have preceded photolysis although oxygen-detoxification mechanisms almost certainly existed long before the evolution of either of these pathways. For example, by reference to Fig. 1–7, antioxidants such as carotenes and vitamin E (an isoprene derivative) are thought to have evolved early in life forms. Similarly CO_2-fixing enzymes such as ribulose 1,5 biphosphate carboxylase also evolved early in living cells, but this enzyme *can* act as an oxygenase under appropriate conditions. Moreover, it seems highly probable that many of the dehydrogenase enzymes of the tricarboxylic acid cycle had evolved prior to aerobic conditions, although at that time they were not linked to an electron transport chain terminating in a cytochrome oxidase – the most efficient means of 'eliminating' oxygen. Instead a number of alternative oxygen-eliminating pathways involving dehydrogenases may have been tried out in response to increasing concentrations of oxygen in the atmosphere. One possibility suggested by de Duve and Baudhuin (1966) (Fig. 1–10) is that catalases and oxidases, present in pre-aerobic times, played a significant role in the transition period, particularly as the presence of molecular oxygen would provide an alternative means of regenerating NAD^+ (nicotinamide adenine dinucleotide) from its reduced form in the cytosol. The normal anaerobic process of regeneration being to convert pyruvate to alcohol (alcoholic fermentation) or pyruvate to lactate (glycolysis). The scheme outlined in Fig. 1–10 shows how NAD^+ *could* be regenerated through a 'peroxisome' pathway using substrates commonly available to primitive life and disposing of small quantities of oxygen at the same time. Another possibility is that bacterial bioluminescence (the production of cold light) is a by-product of oxygen detoxification. Again, this pathway (Fig. 1–11) would not only eliminate oxygen, since the enzyme luciferase has a high affinity for oxygen, but also regenerate NAD^+ from its reduced form. Furthermore, it only requires the alternative link-up of flavins with coenzyme Q and the cytochromes to form the basic elements of the present-day electron transport chain.

However, it would not have been too long before strictly aerobic forms had evolved, using oxidative phosphorylation as the major

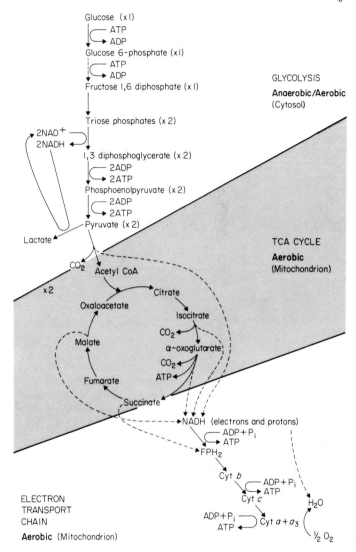

Fig. 1–9 Glycolysis, tricarboxylic acid cycle and electron transport.

pathway for generating ATP and in doing so totally degrading sugars to carbon dioxide and water. In the first aerobic prokaryotes, the same electron transport chain was probably employed in both respiration and photosynthesis, as in some of the present-day purple non-sulphur bacteria such as *Rhodopseudomonas spheroides*, which even uses the same type of oxidase (cytochromes $a + a_3$) as

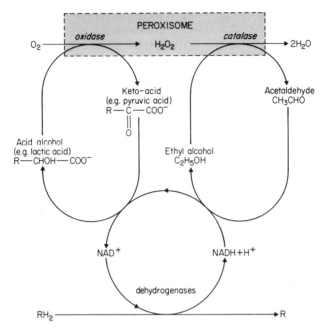

Fig. 1–10 Postulated 'removal' of oxygen via oxidases and catalases. (After de Duve, C. and Baudhuin, P. (1966). *Physiol. Rev.*, **46**, 323–57.)

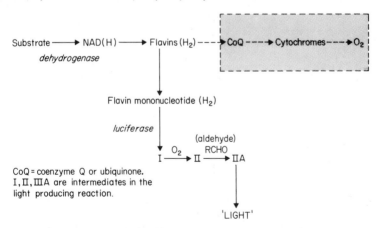

Fig. 1–11 Bacterial Bioluminescence. (After Hastings, J. W. and Nealson, K. H. (1977). *Ann. Rev. Microbiol.*, **31**, 549–96.)

eukaryotic mitochondria (Fig. 1–12). That the respiratory and photosynthetic pathways are related is further emphasized by the common features exhibited by the two types of systems. For example, the first electron carrier in both pathways is a quinone followed by *b*- and *c*- type cytochromes. Furthermore, the amino acid sequencing studies of DICKERSON *et al.* (1976) have shown a remarkable similarity between the *c*-type cytochromes from photosynthetic bacteria, aerobic bacteria and the mitochondria of eukaryotes. This strongly suggests that the two electron transport chains have a common origin.

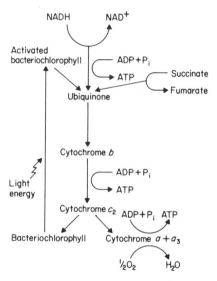

Fig. 1–12 Photosynthetic and respiratory electron transport in *Rhodopseudomonas spheroides*. (After Dickerson, R. E. *et al.* (1976). *J. mol. Biol.*, **100**, 473–91.)

Thus in the Pre-Cambrian of the Archaeozoic era over a thousand million years ago, photo-autotrophs, chemo-autotrophs and heterotrophs were all in existence. Furthermore, although many forms had limited mobility, other prokaryotes increased their mobility and means of dispersal by developing flagella or 'propeller-like' forms (e.g. spirochaetes) or by becoming spore-producing organisms.

A comparison of prokaryotic and eukaryotic metabolic pathways shows that the latter possess additional oxygen-dependent steps in the biosynthesis of sterols, carotenoids and fatty acids. Therefore, it can be reasonably assumed that eukaryotes evolved from prokaryotes during the Pre-Cambrian at a time when the atmosphere was becoming oxygen-rich. In fact, eukaryote-size microfossils have been found in Pre-Cambrian rocks as old as 1.4×10^9 years and nearly all microfossils discovered in rocks older than this are prokaryotic in size. If the classical view regarding the origin of eukaryotic cells is correct (see § 1.1) and evolution did proceed by gradual single-step mutations, then we might

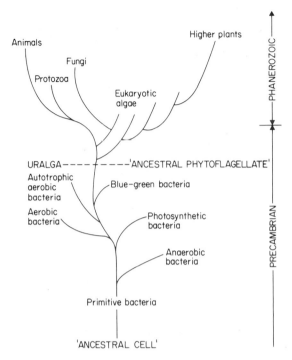

Fig. 1–13 Classical view on the evolution of cellular organisms by gradual accumulation of favourable mutations. (Adapted after MARGULIS, 1970.)

expect to find some fossil record in the world's oldest rocks of the hypothetical ancestor – the 'Uralga', or at least some of the intermediate forms that have been proposed in the evolutionary chain from prokaryotic blue-green bacteria to eukaryotic green algae (see Fig. 1–13). No such organism(s) has yet been found. This does not necessarily disprove the classical view, but it is perhaps surprizing, for example, that fossil evidence is available for photosynthesizing blue-green bacteria in rocks some two thousand million years old, yet fossil records for higher plants (eukaryotic algae) do not appear in any abundance until about 600 million years ago, despite the fact that the mechanism of photosynthesis is essentially similar in both prokaryotes and eukaryotes. Likewise, the discontinuity between the total absence of mitochondria, flagella and mitotic division in prokaryotic blue-green bacteria and their relatively 'sudden' appearance in eukaryotic forms, suggests that alternative explanations to the classical theory should be examined. As MARGULIS (1970) has pointed out – 'the more they (the intermediates) have been sought, the more firmly has the discontinuity between the two forms been established'.

2 The Endosymbiotic Origin of Eukaryotic Cells

2.1 General observations and considerations

It is a fundamental rule in biology that all living organisms are dependent on others to a greater or lesser extent. Heterotrophs are dependent on autotrophs, and autotrophs in turn must rely on decomposers to recycle essential nutrients from dead and decaying matter. But relationships are often much closer than that. Hermit crabs, which themselves use the spent shells of certain molluscs to protect their vulnerable bodies, frequently carry around with them sea anemones, polyzoans and barnacles attached to the outside of the shell. In most cases, there is probably no great advantage accuring to the hermit crab, other than perhaps a rather indirect form of camouflage or distractor. The sea anemones, polyzoans and barnacles, all sessile species, have the advantage that the crab not only takes them to 'pastures new', but may also provide 'crumbs from its own table'. In addition to the passengers on the outside of the shell, it is also common to find inside the shell a small polychaete worm alongside the hermit crab. As with the passengers outside, the close association between crab and worm appears to have little mutual benefit and is a good example of commensalism.

Frequently, however, the relationship between quite different species is totally interdependent or symbiotic. The successful lichens found on rock surfaces, roofs of buildings, gravestones etc., in unpolluted localities, reveal both structurally and physiologically an intimate relationship between a photosynthetic alga and a fungus, which is genetically conferred (SCOTT, 1969). Likewise, members of the plant family Leguminosae, possess nitrogen-fixing bacteria within the cells of their root system; again an example of hereditary symbiosis.

Amongst the ciliate protozoa, such as the 'slipper animalcule' *Paramecium*, are often harboured either endosymbiotic green algae or endosymbiotic bacteria. In one well-investigated example, involving *P. aurelia*, some of the endosymbiotic bacteria (about 20 per cent) produce bright kappa particles, so called because of their refractile properties in the phase-contrast light microscope. When these particles are released from the cytoplasm of the protozoan into the surrounding watery medium they may be taken up by other *Paramecia* via their gullets and food vacuoles. For some, referred to as 'sensitives', the toxic kappa particles are lethal. For others, referred to as 'killers' whose nuclear make-up includes the dominant gene K, kappa-particles have no

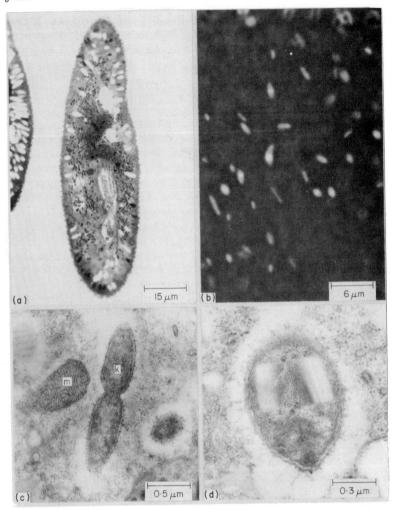

Fig. 2–1 **(a)** Light micrograph (LS) of *Paramecium aurelia* showing numerous kappa symbionts in the cytoplasm. **(b)** Bright phase contrast micrograph showing isolated bright and non-bright kappa symbionts. **(c)** Electron micrograph of a dividing non-bright kappa symbiont sectioned within *P. aurelia*. **(d)** Electron micrograph (LS) through a bright kappa symbiont of *P. aurelia*. The refractile body is in the form of a coiled ribbon. (Courtesy of Dr A. Jurand, Institute of Animal Genetics Edinburgh.)

effect. 'Killer' strains readily harbour bacteria containing kappa-particles and are therefore resistant to their toxins. Thus from laboratory experiments at least, 'killer' strains of *Paramecium* with genotypes KK or Kk can harbour kappa-particles and have a competitive advantage when they are put together with 'sensitive' strains (genotype kk) that can not harbour kappa. One other interesting point is that kappa-bacteria, which are of similar size to mitochondria (approx. 0.5 μm) (see Fig. 2–1), can not be cultured outside the protozoan host cell (PREER *et al.*, 1974).

Another species of *Paramecium* (*P. bursaria*) is green in colour, due to the presence of green endosymbiotic algae of the genus *Chlorella*. The optimal number of *Chlorella* cells in each *Paramecium* is genetically regulated by the host cell (MUSCATINE and POOL, 1979). In addition to nutrient exchange between symbiont and host, the algal cells also have 'diplomatic immunity', because if the *Paramecium* encounters free-living *Chlorella* cells, they are taken up and digested. Morphologically little difference can be detected between the free-living and the symbiotic *Chlorella* cells, yet the latter are recognized as symbionts by the host cell, whereas the former are not. The mechanism of regulation is poorly understood, but whatever it is, it can regulate algal cell division remarkably well with host cell growth. Interestingly in this case, it is possible to culture the algal symbionts when they are isolated from their host, but the host cell will die very quickly if deprived of its guests unless additional nutrients are added to its environment.

Perhaps the most extraordinary of all symbiotic relationships is the case of the flagellate *Myxotricha paradoxa*. Firstly this protozoan is itself a symbiont. It lives in the guts of certain Australian termites and helps these insects digest their woody diet. Closer examination of

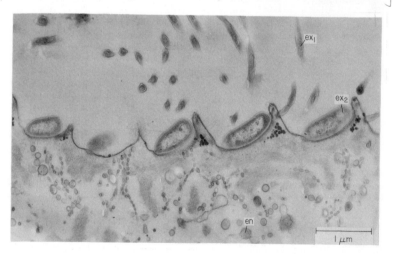

Fig. 2–2 Electronmicrograph of the two exosymbionts (ex_1 and ex_2) and one endosymbiont (en) of *Myxotricha paradoxa*. (Courtesy of Dr A. V. Grimstone, 1964, *Proc. Roy. Soc. B*, **159**, 668.)

Myxotricha, however, reveals that it in turn is host to three different bacterial symbionts; two exosymbionts on the surface of the organism and one endosymbiont inside. Outwardly, *Myxotricha* appears to have four large flagella at the leading end of the cell and numerous small flagella or cilia over the whole surface. It turns out from a detailed electron microscopic examination (Fig. 2–2) that the so-called small flagella are actually spirochaetes – elongated, motile bacteria. Furthermore, the way in which these spirochaetes are attached to the surface of the host is aided by another kind of bacterium, which is also anchored to the surface. As regards the endosymbiont, its function is unknown.

In addition to protozoa, many multicellular animals have also evolved symbiotic relationships with bacteria and algae. Many of the

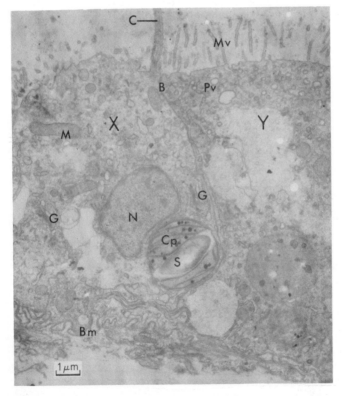

Fig. 2–3 Isolated, but fully functional chloroplasts within the gut cells of the marine sea-slug *Elysia viridis*. X and Y, two cells; B, border; Bm, border membrane; C, cilium; G, Golgi bodies; Cp, chloroplast; M, mitochondria; N, nucleus; Pr, pinocytotic vesicles; S, starch grannule. (Reproduced by kind permission of Dr D. L. Taylor, 1968, *J. Mar. Biol. Assoc.* (UK), **48**, 1–15.)

deep-sea fish are able to emit species-specific light patterns by harbouring carefully arranged arrays of symbiotic, bioluminescent bacteria. The clam maintains an algal garden within its mantle. The green hydra (*H. viridis*) gets its colour from the numerous small, spherical green algae called zoochlorellae, which are found living in the large endodermal cells lining the enteron or gut. In one or two bizarre cases, certain marine sea-slugs (e.g. *Elysia viridis*) belonging to the phylum Mollusca have somehow developed a mechanism for retrieving intact and fully functional chloroplasts from their diet of algae (Fig. 2–3). The 'extracted' chloroplasts come to reside in the primitive branching gut of the mollusc and continue to function as photosynthetic organelles for several weeks (SMITH, 1979).

There are therefore numerous examples of symbiotic relationships—many, if not all, maintained or perpetuated on a hereditary basis. Consequently, the suggestion that mitochondria, chloroplasts, flagella, cilia and the mitotic spindle all had an endosymbiotic origin, may not seem too surprizing.

2.2   Did chloroplasts and mitochondria have an endosymbiotic origin?

As long ago as 1890, Altmann suggested that mitochondria, which he called 'bioblasts', were once free-living organisms. Mereschkowsky (1905) proposed a similar origin for plastids. In recent years, MARGULIS (1970) has presented a detailed theory for the origin of the eukaryotic state from a primitive phagocytic amoeboid cell, referred to as the *protoeukaryote*. This protoeukaryote acquired mitochondria and chloroplasts by engulfing, but not digesting aerobic bacteria and blue-green bacteria, so that the relationship between the bacterial cell and its host was an endosymbiotic one. Proponents of the endosymbiotic theory are not agreed on the actual sequence of events but the universal presence of mitochondria in eukaryotes would tend to suggest that the acquisition of mitochondria pre-dated that of chloroplasts (Fig. 2–4).

A great deal of information is now available concerning the similarities between mitochondria, chloroplasts and contemporary prokaryotes. Comparisons of analogous structures show that mitochondria and chloroplasts exhibit more than a few prokaryotic features. For instance, in prokaryotes, respiratory electron transport pathways are localized in the cell membrane or in structures derived from this membrane (*mesosomes*) whereas, in eukaryotes, these pathways are located within the inner membrane of the mitochondrion. Similarly, the photosynthetic electron transport system of eukaryotes is located in chloroplast *thylakoid* lamellae, which are flattened sacs or vesicles originating from the inner chloroplast membrane. Cyanobacteria also contain thylakoids, but these photosynthetic structures are

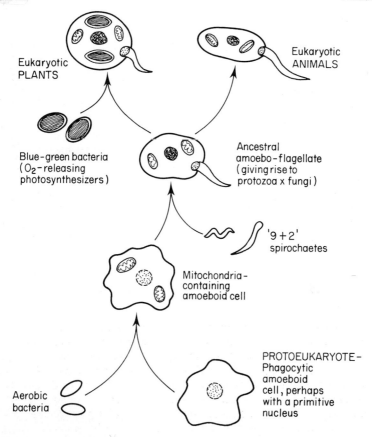

Fig. 2–4 The postulated evolution of eukaryotic cells by serial endosymbiosis. (Adapted from MARGULIS, 1970.)

derived from the cell membrane, as are the intracellular vesicles (*chromatophores*) and lamellae of photosynthetic anaerobic bacteria. Also, with the possible exception of the nucleus, mitochondria and chloroplasts are the only eukaryotic organelles that are delimited by persistent double membranes. The outer membranes of mitochondria and chloroplasts appear to have structural and biochemical similarities with the endoplasmic reticulum, which, in the opinion of some biologists, is an extension of the cell membrane. TAYLOR (1974) suggests that, as the endoplasmic reticulum essentially forms a boundary between the inside and outside of the cell, the inner components of mitochondria and chloroplasts can be considered as being outside the cell. This is, of course, compatible with an endosymbiotic origin for these organelles since nearly all contemporary endosymbionts are sequestered within endoplasmic reticulum.

The serial endosymbiotic theory (or S.E.T. for short) predicts that mitochondria and chloroplasts might retain some remnants of their past autonomy. It was once thought that it might be possible to isolate growing mitochondria in an artificial medium. In fact, Wallin (1922) reported that he had successfully cultured mitochondria outside of the cell but this claim was later disproved when it was shown that his results could be accounted for by bacterial contamination. The failure to isolate growing mitochondria might explain why the endosymbiotic theory lost its appeal and was forgotten for many years. In 1951, however, Chiba demonstrated the presence of DNA in chloroplasts and later Nass and Nass (1963) showed that mitochondria also contain DNA. Here again, the organelles were found to exhibit certain prokaryotic features. Firstly, under the electron microscope the organellar DNAs are seen to have a fibrillar structure very similar to that of the prokaryotic *nucleoid*. Also, like prokaryotic nucleoid DNA, mitochondrial (mt) and chloro-plast (cl) DNA molecules are circular and, unlike eukaryotic nuclear DNA, they do not appear to be complexed with histone proteins (Fig. 2–5). With few exceptions, most animal cell mtDNAs have a contour length in the order of $5\,\mu m$, which corresponds to a molecular mass of

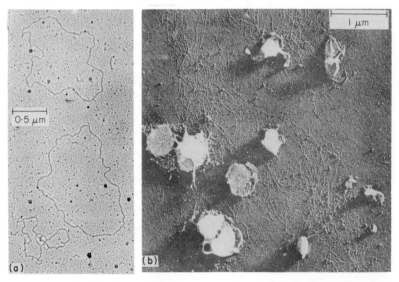

Fig. 2–5 (a) Mitochondrial DNA from rat liver. (b) Portion of osmotically disrupted spinach chloroplasts showing DNA strands associated with membranes. ((a) Courtesy of Dr M. M. K. Nass, 1966, *Proc. Natl. Acad. Sci.*, **56**, 1215–22, and (b) courtesy of Drs C. L. Woodcock and H. Fernandez – Moran, 1968, *J. mol. Biol.*, **31**, 627–31.)

about 10^7 daltons. However, mtDNAs from plants and the yeast *Saccharomyces cerevisiae* appear to be nearer 30 μm in length and clDNAs are even longer (40–60 μm). Although the size of clDNA is comparable with the DNA of a bacterium or a cyanobacterium, mtDNA is nearer in contour length to that found in viruses, and on size alone is quite definitely incapable of coding for all the mitochondrial proteins. Indeed, we now know that mtDNA codes for no more than 5 per cent of the total mitochondrial protein content and, similarly, the chloroplast genetic system contributes only a fraction of the total chloroplast protein. The contributions made by the organelle genetic systems to their own assembly are summarized in Table 2.

If mitochondria and chloroplasts are the descendants of endosymbiotic prokaryotes the relationship between these organelles and the host cell must represent a very advanced form of symbiosis. This 'advanced symbiosis' is further emphasized by other aspects of organelle autonomy. For instance, mitochondria and chloroplasts exhibit autonomy at the level of DNA replication, RNA synthesis, and protein synthesis, even though the bulk of the structural and enzymic machinery for these processes is supplied by the nuclear genetic system. Of these, organelle protein synthesis has been most extensively studied and has demonstrated further prokaryotic features of mitochondria and chloroplasts.

The translation of messenger RNA (transcribed from DNA) into the amino acid sequence of a protein takes place on particles called *ribosomes* which are often seen grouped as chains or *polyribosomes*. Ribosomes can be dissociated into two subunits – large and small. These subunits are composed of structural or ribosomal (r) RNA molecules complexed with proteins. The size of the ribosome particles, their subunits and component rRNAs have been determined by a technique known as analytical ultracentrifugation. The rate of sedimentation is a measure of the size, shape and density of a particle or macromolecule

Table 2 Organelle components known to be coded for by the mitochondrial and chloroplast DNAs.

Mitochondrial	*Chloroplast*
3 subunits of cytochrome aa_3	Large subunit of ribulose 1, 5 biphosphate carboxylase present in the stroma
1 subunit of cytochrome b	9 of the 33 major polypeptides of the thylakoid membranes
? 4 subunits of ATPase	Ribosomal RNAs
1 ribosomal protein	Transfer RNAs
Ribosomal RNAs	? Ribosomal proteins (one or a few)
Transfer RNAs	Elongation factors (catalyse peptide chain elongation)
	? Some envelope proteins

and is expressed as the *sedimentation coefficient* or *S value*. The larger the S value, the greater is the density, size and shape of the particle and the converse is true for small S values. A comparison of ribosomes from organelles, bacteria and the eukaryotic cytoplasm (Table 3) reveals a close similarity between bacteria and chloroplasts in the size of subunit and major rRNA species. That is to say, these ribosomes have smaller S values than those of the eukaryotic cytoplasm. On the other hand, mitochondrial ribosomes are less uniform in size, ranging from 60 S in the toad *Xenopus* to 80 S in the ciliated protozoan *Tetrahymena*. Thus although it would appear that chloroplast ribosomes are more like those of prokaryotes than they are to the ribosomes in the eukaryotic cytoplasm, it is not possible to say the same about mitochondrial ribosomes when S values alone are considered. However, the diversity in mitochondrial ribosomes compared to the uniformity in size of chloroplast ribosomes is in agreement with the S.E.T. as proposed by MARGULIS, because it is envisaged that the ancestral mitochondrion invaded the host cell *before* the ancestral chloroplast (Fig. 2–4), so giving mitochondria more time in which to diversify.

Table 3   S values for ribosomes of various organisms and their organelles.

Organism		Subunits			rRNAs	
		Monomer	*Large*	*Small*	*Large*	*Small*
E. coli		70	50	30	23	16
Yeast	– cytoplasm	82	61	38	25	18
	– mitochondria	72–80	50–60	37–40	22	15
Tetrahymena	– cytoplasm	80	60	40	26	17
	– mitochondria	80	55	55	21	14
Euglena	– chloroplast	68–70	46–50	29–30	22	17
Green alga	– cytoplasm	83	58	40	25	18
	– chloroplast	68–70	52–54	37–41	23	16
Higher plant	– cytoplasm	78	56	36	25	18
	– chloroplast	70	45	32	23	16
Xenopus	– mitochondria	60	43	32	21	13

One of the predictions of the S.E.T. is that mitochondrial and chloroplast ribosomes will exhibit sensitivity to antibiotics that inhibit bacterial protein synthesis, whilst being resistant to drugs that affect specifically the ribosomes of the eukaryotic cytoplasm. This prediction has been generally confirmed, though not conclusively, as shown in Table 4.

Another notable similarity in the translation systems of prokaryotes and eukaryotic organelles is the way in which polypeptide synthesis is initiated. In mitochondria, chloroplasts and bacteria, a formylation step (i.e. the addition of an HCHO group catalysed by the enzyme transformylase) follows charging of the tRNA with methionine. By

Table 4　Effect of inhibitors on protein synthesis.

Inhibitor	Cytoplasmic	Mitochondrial chloroplast	Bacterial
Anisomycin	+	−	−
Cycloheximide	+	−	−
Emetine	+	+/−?	−
Mikamycin	−	+	+
Chloramphenicol	−	+	+
Erythromycin	−	+/−?	+
Lincomycin	−	+/−?	+

+ inhibition;　− no inhibition.
+/−? mitochondria from some species inhibited whilst those from others are not.

contrast, in the eukaryotic cytoplasm the formylation step is omitted and met-tRNA acts as the polypeptide chain initiator (Fig. 2–6).

An important point that emerges from these comparisons of protein synthesizing systems is the uniqueness of the eukaryotic cytoplasmic translation apparatus. This suggests two possible hypotheses:

either 1) Whilst preserving those prokaryotic features of the organellar translation systems, the eukaryotic protein synthesis apparatus of the cytoplasm has not been subjected to the same constraints. This hypothesis is compatible with an endosymbiotic or a non-endosymbiotic origin for the eukaryote line.

or 2) The line leading to the evolution of the ancestral mitochondrion and chloroplast was different to that which gave rise to the phagocytic host cell or protoeukaryote. This can be explained only in terms of the S. E. T. WOESE and FOX (1977) have proposed that the eukaryote and prokaryote lines have evolved separately from a primitive group of organisms, referred to as *progenotes*, which had an unreliable translation system. They argue that the ancestral prokaryote and the protoeukaryote independently solved the problem of unreliable translation, but by different means. Hence the differences in the two types of translation system.

So far, we have been concerned only with phenotypic comparisons

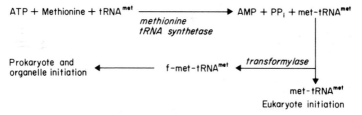

Fig. 2–6　Comparison of polypeptide chain initiation in prokaryotic and eukaryotic cells.

between prokaryotes, organelles and eukaryotic cytoplasm. A more informative approach to the problem is to measure the relatedness of various organisms and their subcellular structures by comparing amino acid sequences of homologous proteins and base sequences of homologous structural genes or their RNA transcription products. Dickerson has shown that prokaryotic, chloroplast and mitochondrial c-type cytochromes share so many similar amino acid sequences that they are almost certainly descended from a common protein ancestor (see Chapter 1). This strongly suggests that a phylogenetic relationship exists between the prokaryotes and eukaryote organelles. The idea has been explored further by Woese and his collaborators who have developed the technique of 'oligonucleotide cataloguing', i.e. a study of small groups of base sequences. This technique essentially involves enzymic splitting of the large rRNA molecules from various organisms and organelles into smaller oligonucleotide fragments of different sizes, followed by base sequencing of these oligomers. The oligonucleotide sequences of the rRNA from one source are then compared with those of rRNAs isolated from other sources to see how many sequences they have in common. For example, chloroplast 16 S rRNA from *Porphyridium* (a red alga) contains a pentamer nucleotide sequence of CAACG—which is also present in the 16 S rRNAs from the cyanobacterium *Anacystis nidulans* and the bacterial species *Bacillus subtilis* and *Escherichia coli*. However, this sequence is absent from *Porphyridium* cytosolic 18 S rRNA (Fig. 2–7). In fact, the chloroplast 16 S rRNAs from *Porphyridium* and *Euglena* possess a large number of ologonucleotide sequences that are also present in prokaryote 16 S rRNA but appear to be less common in cytosolic 18 S rRNA species. Thus, chloroplast 16 S rRNAs show extensive homology with prokaryote 16 S rRNAs but very little homology with cytosolic 18 S rRNA molecules. Similarly, mitochondrial rRNA has been shown to be much more like that of the prokaryotes than that of the cytosol, as can be seen from the oligonucleotide sequence comparisons summarized in Table 5.

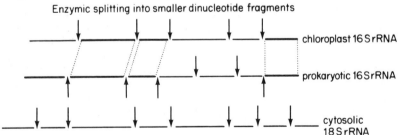

Enzymic splitting into smaller dinucleotide fragments

chloroplast 16 S rRNA

prokaryotic 16 S rRNA

cytosolic 18 S rRNA

Fig. 2–7 Diagrammatic representation of 'oligonucleotide cataloguing'. Dotted lines indicate homologous sections.

Table 5 A comparison of oligonucleotide sequences of chloroplast and mitochondrial rRNAs with homologous rRNA species.

	Porphyridium chloroplast	Euglena gracilis chloroplast	*Wheat mitochondrial*
Cyanophytes			
Anacystis nidulans 16 S	+	+	
Gloeocapsa alpicola 16 S			+
Bacteria			
Bacillus subtilis 16 S	+	+	+
Escherichia coli 16 S	+	+	+
Rhodopseudomonas spheroides 16 S		+	+
Red alga			
Porphyridium chloroplast 16 S		+	+
Porphyridium cytoplasmic 18 S	−		
Yeast cytoplasmic 18 S		−	
Wheat cytoplasmic 18 S		−	−

+ homology, i.e. share a large number of oligonucleotide sequences in common (N ⩾ 5).
− little or no homology, i.e. share very few, if any, of the same oligonucleotide sequences (N ⩾ 5). Blank not compared. Data compiled from various sources.

Oligonucleotide sequencing of rRNAs leads us to conclude that mitochondria and chloroplasts almost certainly had a prokaryotic origin. Unfortunately, even this quantitative approach to the problem does not enable us to decide conclusively between the hypotheses outlined on page 25. Whilst this evidence is in good agreement with the S. E. T., it does not rule out the possibility of a non-endosymbiotic theory for the origin of eukaryotic cells. However, this point will be taken up again in the last chapter of the book.

2.3   The possible ancestry of chloroplasts and mitochondria

If the eukaryote organelles evolved from free-living prokaryotes, as proposed by the S. E. T., we might expect to find extant prokaryotes resembling the ancestral forms that gave rise to mitochondria and chloroplasts through endosymbiosis. Most aerobic bacteria are found to possess at least a few mitochondrial features, especially in their respiratory chains. However, rarely does an aerobic bacterium contain a respiratory chain with near identical features to that of the mitochondrion. One exception is *Paracoccus denitrificans* (Fig. 2–8). The existence of *Paracoccus* means that it is possible that similar types lived 1500 million years ago and that the transition to an endosymbiotic protomitochondrion would have been biochemically feasible.

Although the majority of mitochondria contain respiratory pathways

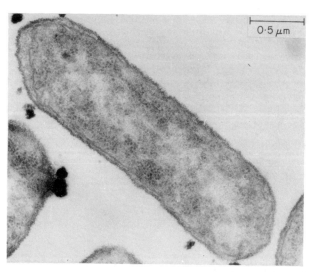

Fig. 2–8 Electronmicrograph of *Paracoccus denitrificans*, a bacterium with an electron transport system similar to mitochondria. (Courtesy of J. M. WHATLEY *et al.*, 1979.)

with very similar components, the same cannot be said of chloroplast photosynthetic chains. All chloroplasts contain chlorophyll *a* but they vary according to the nature of their secondary photosynthetic pigments (Table 6; see also HALL and RAO, 1981).

RAVEN (1970) has taken the view that if chloroplasts evolved through endosymbiosis then those of contemporary plant groups are probably descended from different endosymbiotic prokaryotic algae. It follows from this that the prokaryotic algae that gave rise to the chloroplasts might also be ancestral to the free-living prokaryotic algae of today. In Table 6 it can be seen that the blue-green bacteria (Cyanophyta) possess phycobilins, which occur only in this group of prokaryotes and in the eukaryotic red algae (Rhodophyta) and flagellated cryptophytes. Moreover, the thylakoids of red algae and blue-green bacteria are not stacked into *grana* as in most other types of higher plant chloroplast. The idea that ancient blue-green bacteria were ancestral to red algal

Table 6 Distribution of secondary photosynthetic pigments in prokaryotes and eukaryotes. All forms possess chlorophyll *a*. (From WHATLEY *et al.*, 1979.)

Pigment	Prokaryote		Eukaryote
Phycobilins	Cyanophyta	⟶	Rhodophyta
Chlorophyll *b*	Prochlorophyta	⟶	Chlorophyta and land plants
Chlorophyll *c*	?	⟶	Chromophyta

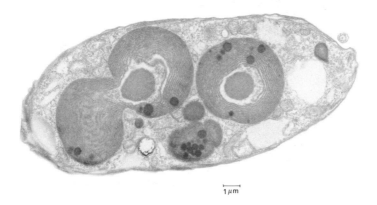

1 μm

Fig. 2–9 Electronmicrograph of *Cyanophora paradoxa*. (Courtesy of W. T. Hall, in SCOTT, 1969.)

chloroplasts is rendered even more likely when it is realized that present-day blue-greens are often found as endosymbionts in amoebae, and flagellated protozoa lacking chloroplasts. A striking example is the 'green' alga *Glaucocystis nostochinearum*, which has blue-green bacterial endosymbionts in place of chloroplasts. Another example of particular interest is the anomalous eukaryotic alga, *Cyanophora paradoxa*, which harbours photosynthetic structures called cyanelles with properties intermediate between blue-green bacteria and red algal chloroplasts (Fig. 2–9). That is, their photosynthetic pigments and thylakoids appear to be very similar to red algal chloroplasts but they possess cell wall remnants characteristic of the blue-green bacteria. The existence of these 'protochloroplasts' argues strongly in favour of the endosymbiotic theory.

Until recently, it was thought that the group of prokaryotes from which the chloroplasts of green algae (Chlorophyta) were supposed to be descended had become extinct. But the discovery of the prokaryotic alga, *Prochloron* (Fig. 2–10), has now provided a possible green algal chloroplast precursor. As with the chloroplasts of the Chlorophyta, Euglenophyta and land plants, *Prochloron* contains chlorophylls *a* and *b* but lacks phycobilins, and shows stacking of the thylakoid membranes. LEWIN (1976) has proposed that this prokaryotic green cell, which is found as an extracellular symbiont within sea squirt colonies, be placed in a new algal division, the Prochlorophyta.

There are reasons for thinking that the origins of chromophyte chloroplasts, might not have been as straightforward as those of the Rhodophyta and Chlorophyta. Chloroplasts of the Rhodophyta and

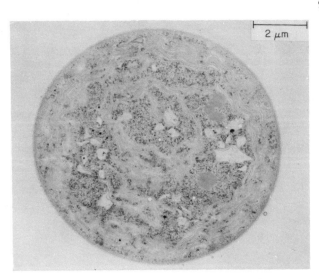

Fig. 2–10 The prokaryotic alga *Prochloron* with chlorophyll *a* and chlorophyll *b*, an extracellular symbiont of a didemnid. (Courtesy of Dr J. M. Whatley, University of Oxford.)

Chlorophyta have two surrounding membranes but those of the Chromophyta have four. A careful examination of the chromophyte cytoplasm also reveals the presence of structures resembling ribosomes and a primitive nucleus or *nucleomorph* in the space separating the outer and inner pairs of chloroplast membranes. WHATLEY and co-workers (1979) suggest that the chromophyte chloroplasts were once *eukaryotic* endosymbionts and that the space between the two pairs of membranes was once the cytoplasm of the endosymbiont.

If the number of chloroplast membranes is an indicator of the evolutionary origins of these organelles we have also to explain how the chloroplasts of the Euglenophyta came to have three encircling membranes. The observation that some marine worms possess algal chloroplast endosymbionts (see § 2.1) led Whatley and her colleagues to propose that the chloroplasts of the Euglenophyta have been captured from an organism with chloroplasts containing chlorophylls *a* and *b* – a green alga, perhaps? These theories are summarized in Fig. 2–11.

The scheme proposed in Fig. 2–11 is attractive, but there is a puzzle with respect to the subsequent evolution of the cell wall in Rhodophyta, Chlorophyta and Chromophyta. Normally, it is assumed that the host cell was phagocytic in order to engulf the endosymbiont in the first place. Phagocytotic cells do not posses cell walls. Having acquired a photosynthetic endosymbiont, however, the host cell may not have needed to remain phagocytic, i.e. it might resemble the Euglenophyceae, which have no cell wall. But what were the selective pressures favouring the

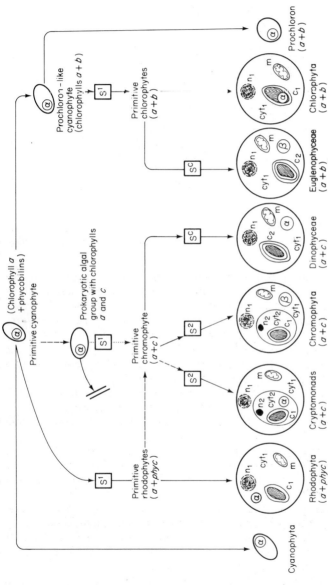

Adapted from Whatley *et al* Proc. Roy. Soc. Lond. (1979) & Whatley N.Y.A.S Symposium (1980)

Fig. 2–11 The possible evolutionary origins of the various plant and algal groups. S¹, endosymbiosis with an amoeboid-like protoeukaryote; S², endosymbiosis with a photosynthetic eukaryote; Sᶜ, capture of a chloroplast through endosymbiosis; c₁, chloroplast; c₂, isolated chloroplast endosymbiont; m, mitochondrion; n₁, nucleus of host cell; n₂, nucleus of endosymbiont; cyt₁, host cytoplasm; cyt₂, endosymbiont cytoplasm; α or β, site and type of carbohydrate storage product.

development of the cell wall in the algal groups after endosymbiosis had
been established?

2.4   The protoeukaryote and the origin of the nucleus

If we can find extant models of the ancient prokaryotes that
supposedly gave rise to the ancestral mitochondrion and chloroplast,
then we might also find a present-day model of the protoeukaryote.
WHATLEY (1976) has described how the giant amoeba, *Pelomyxa
palustris* harbours at least two kinds of endosymbiotic bacteria but lacks
mitochondria and, whilst possessing nuclei, does not undergo cell
division by conventional mitosis. The large bacteria of *Pelomyxa* (Fig.
2–12) are permanent endosymbionts which become closely associated
with the host nuclei at division so that the daughter amoebae each
inherit a population of bacteria. This relationship is clearly very similar
to the sort of symbiosis that might have led to the evolution of
mitochondria. That the acquisition of bacterial endosymbionts by the

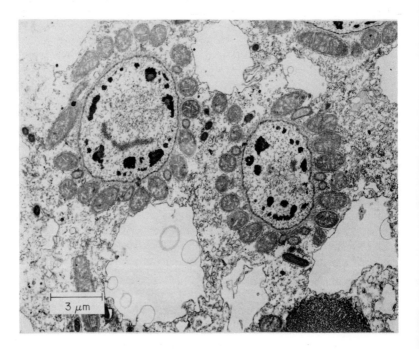

Fig. 2–12 Electronmicrograph showing a section through *Pelomyxa
palustris*, a multinucleate amoeba with aggregations of bacteria around nuclei.
(Courtesy of Dr J. M. Whatley, University of Oxford.)

protoeukaryote might not have taken very long is indicated by the work of JEONS and JEONS (1976), who infected cells of *Amoeba proteus* with bacteria and after nine years found that the amoebae had an absolute dependence for these bacteria, i.e. they were unable to live without them.

But how do proponents of the serial endosymbiotic theory visualize the organization of the genetic material in the protoeukaryote? Was it essentially prokaryotic, with the DNA organized into multiple copies or nucleoids, or was it essentially eukaryotic with the DNA contained within a single structure resembling a primitive nucleus?

MARGULIS (1970) would seem to favour the first alternative . . . 'by the middle Pre-Cambrian, we had a primitive eukaryote, aerobic and motile. It contained mitochondria and cortical spirochaetes; DNA was distributed in the cell as in all bacterial nucleoids.' Strictly speaking, from this description the organism was not a eukaryote, since it did not contain a true nucleus, but be that as it may. By turning once again to *Pelomyxa palustris* we may find a convenient model, since this primitive cell is multinucleate. That is, each nucleus (unlike a nucleoid) possesses a nuclear membrane with nuclear pores, yet each nucleus probably houses identical amounts of genetic information essential for the maintenance of new daughter amoebae. In this respect, *Pelomyxa* may represent one of the earliest mechanisms developed by living organisms to distribute somewhat greater amounts of DNA evenly to daughter cells without the use of conventional mitosis.

Precisely how *Pelomyxa* replicates and segregates its genetic material, without an obvious mitotic spindle, is unknown at present. Perhaps the development of nuclear membranes provides the necessary attachment points for DNA replication. It would also be interesting to know whether the DNA is in the form of linear chromosomes and whether microtubular elements are involved at any stage of division or not. Clearly, for any cell with the ability to phagocytose over its whole surface, the selection pressure favouring internal membrane attachment sites, rather than the bounding cell membrane (as in conventional prokaryotes), would be strong – a point taken up again by CAVALIER-SMITH (1975) in Chapter 3. Exactly how the internal membranes so characteristic of eukaryotic cells evolved is a controversial issue. Margulis believes that judging from the complementation of metabolic pathways in certain extant symbioses (particularly the algal/fungal partnership in lichens), the mitochondrial-host symbiosis was the essential feature leading to the biosynthetic steps necessary to form the typical eukaryotic membranes with their high proportion of sterols and sterol-esters. Other views on this matter are discussed in Chapter 3.

Apart from the presence of nuclei, internal membranes and membrane-bound organelles, eukaryotic cells generally have greater size and a greater number of chromosomes. The origin of the spindle and mitosis was not a consequence of this, but an essential prerequisite. PICKET-HEAPS

(1974) has gone so far as to say that 'the origin of eukaryotic cells cannot be dissociated from the problem of accounting for the origin of mitosis'. It is to this matter that we now turn our attention, with particular reference to the S. E. T.

2.5   Microtubule systems

Unlike the majority of prokaryotes, most eukaryotes possess micro-tubules which are hollow, tube-like structures, 20–30 nm in diameter and composed of subunits of the protein *tubulin*. Microtubules can be shortened or lengthened by the removal or addition of tubulin subunits. *Cilia* and *flagella* are hairlike cell projections that possess a '9 + 2' pattern' of microtubules (Fig. 2–13).

In cross-section, there are 9 pairs of microtubules surrounding a central pair. Only the outer 9 filaments extend (as triplets) into the cytoplasm forming a structure called the *basal body*. Cilia and flagella are essentially short and long versions of the same structure and they are used for cell propulsion or for moving the surrounding liquid over a cell which occupies a fixed position (e.g. an epithelial cell lining the trachea). Interestingly, a similar '9 + 0' array of the basal body is also found in *centrioles*, which are organelles that act as centres for the organization of microtubules of the mitotic spindle. The relationship between the

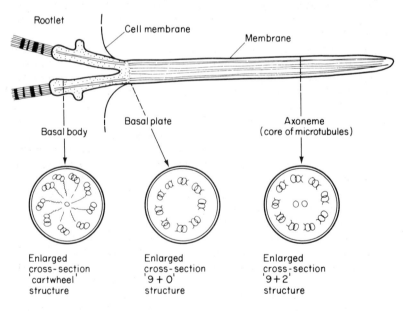

Fig. 2–13   The structure of the eukaryotic cilium and basal body.

centriole and basal body is further emphasized by the observation that during spermatogenesis, a centriole becomes a true basal body and gives rise to a flagellum ('sperm-tail'). The '9+2' and '9+0' homologues found in eukaryotic cells have been referred to as *undulipodia* to distinguish them from prokaryotic flagella, which have a simple structure composed of *flagellin*, a protein that is insensitive to the tubulin-binding drug colchicine. (Colchicine is often used to 'fix' mitotically dividing cells at metaphase.)

Only one group of prokaryotes appear to possess structures resembling microtubules, namely the *Spirochaetes*. Amongst this group of motile, helically shaped bacteria, the species *Pillotina calotermitidis* has 'microtubules' that are often arranged longitudinally, are about 25 nm in cross-sectional diameter, and appear to be colchicine-sensitive (MARGULIS *et al.*, 1978, 1979). Furthermore, several species of spirochaetes are regularly attached to protista via special attachment sites and when present in groups often beat in synchrony. One classic example (mentioned in Chapter 1), is the symbiont *Myxotricha paradoxa* found in termite guts.

Margulis suggests that spirochaetes became symbiotically associated with primitive protists, with the spirochaetes conferring motility on their host in return for a guaranteed supply of nutrients. It is envisaged that the spirochaete attachment sites eventually became basal bodies and other undulipodia were evolved after the ingestion of the symbionts and the transfer of their genetic information to the host cell, possibly by means of a virus.

The sequence of events in nucleated organisms leading to the formation of mitotically dividing cells capable of movement by cilia and flagella, is proposed by Margulis as follows: 1) amitotic amoeboid cell (e.g. *Pelomyxa*) ⟶ 2) amitotic flagellate or amoeboflagellate (an amoeboid cell with an endosymbiotic spirochaete) ⟶ 3) mitotic amoeboid cell ⟶ 4) mitotic flagellate cell. If the S. E. T. is correct on this point, then once again extant models might be found. For example, in the amoeboflagellate *Naegleria*, no true mitotic apparatus has ever been seen at any stage in the life cycle. Cell division is restricted to the amoeboid phase, but centrioles, spindle apparatus and basal bodies are absent during this phase. Nevertheless, in the flagellate phase, basal bodies are clearly evident and genetic information for making such basal bodies and flagellae must be available in the 'host' genome. The evolutionary interpretation of this is that *Naegleria* represents a primitive stage following the initial host endosymbiont relationship. By contrast, amongst the more advanced rhodophytes, such as *Polysiphonia* a mitotic spindle exists, but like all rhodophytes there is a total absence of any motile (ciliated) cells. It is argued that rhodophytes may have lost cilia and flagella as a secondary feature, although in our view there appears to be no good reason why this should happen.

2.6   Other considerations—gene transfer from endosymbiont to host

Implicit in the S. E. T. is that during the course of evolution there was a transfer of genetic information from the mitochondrion and chloroplast to the nucleus. That prokaryotic DNA can integrate and be maintained in a eukaryotic genome has been demonstrated by HINNEN *et al.* (1978), who transformed yeast cells that required the amino acid leucine for growth (*leu*$^-$) with the yeast *leu*$^+$ gene linked with a piece of DNA from *Escherichia coli*. Both the *leu*$^+$ gene and *E. coli* DNA were shown to integrate into the yeast nuclear genome. This elegant experiment suggests that transfer of genetic information from the protomitochondrion to the primitive eukaryotic nucleus would have been possible. Perhaps the most compelling evidence for gene transfer from the mitochondrion to the nucleus has been obtained by studies on the mitochondrial ATPase from yeast and another fungus, *Neurospora*; (BORST and GRIVELL, 1978). One of the subunits of this complex binds a reagent called *DCCD* (dicyclohexylcarbodimide). Amino acid sequencing and physical analyses of the DCCD-binding proteins from yeast and *Neurospora* has shown that they are undoubtedly homologous. However, the yeast DCCD-binding protein is coded for by the mt-DNA, whilst that of *Neurospora* is determined by the nuclear genome. Of course, these findings do not offer conclusive evidence that gene transfer has taken place, but the evidence is certainly consistent with the S. E. T.

To conclude, serial endosymbiosis seems to offer a plausible explanation for the evolution of eukaryotic cells, especially with regard to the origin of chloroplasts and mitochondria. However, much of the evidence used in support of the S. E. T. can just as easily be accounted for by non-endosymbiotic theories. Indeed, some features of eukaryotic organelles can be more readily explained by alternative hypotheses and these are examined in the next chapter.

3 Alternative Theories

3.1 Introduction

The endosymbiotic theory for the origin of eukaryotic organelles is undoubtedly a fascinating concept and, at first sight its arguments can be compelling. However, the theory is by no means proven. Furthermore, the endosymbiotic theory has not addressed itself quite so keenly to one of the more remarkable features of eukaryotic cells, namely the evolution of the nucleus and the processes of mitotic and meiotic cell division. These processes require enlargement and more orderly organization of the genetic material as well as more sophisticated means for distribution of the DNA complement at cell division than exists in prokaryotic cells. In this chapter we describe alternative theories for the origin of mitochondria and consider the evolution of some of the other features of eukaryotic cells which distinguish them from prokaryotes.

3.2 The plasmid theory for mitochondrial origin

A great deal of the debate concerning the origin of the eukaryotic state has revolved around the origin of mitochondria, the organelles specialized for oxidative phosphorylation of ADP to ATP. This revival of interest has undoubtedly occurred because the mitochondrion has been found to contain its own characteristic DNA with its crucial, although quantitatively small, contribution to the assembly of the functional organelle. The discovery of a machinery for transcription and translation of the information encoded in mitochondrial DNA, which is quite distinct from that involved in processing nuclear DNA information content has also contributed to the considerable level of interest in the origins of these systems. RAFF and MAHLER (1975), in arriving at their ideas for the evolutionary origin of mitochondria, have inspected closely the comparative molecular biologies of the nucleic acid and protein synthesizing systems present in eukaryotes and prokaryotes. This contrasts with the approach of many of the proponents of the endosymbiont hypothesis whose contributions until very recently have been based to a large extent on cytological investigations. This has led Raff and Mahler to put forward the view that mitochondria have evolved within a prokaryote (or protoeukaryote) cell without an input from any other organism. In short, their theory suggests that vesicles initially arose by invagination of the bacterial limiting membrane and that subsequently a fragment of DNA capable of generating the macromolecular synthesizing systems was incorporated into the vesicles. The theory is based upon the behaviour exhibited by certain genetic elements known as *plasmids*. Plasmids are autonomous genetic elements (small circles of DNA) found in almost every type of bacterial cell. Plasmids are capable of an independent, self-replicating existence inside the bacterial cell, quite separate from the replication of the larger circular DNA (chromosome) of the host cell. Additionally however, there are certain plasmids, that can integrate into and out of the host cell's DNA, with the possibility of exchanging genetic material between the plasmid and the chromosomes.

The mitochondrial DNA of eukaryotes has certain features which resemble those of prokaryotic genomes (see Fig. 2–5). Both are double-stranded, covalently closed, circular, supercoiled molecules with attachment sites to their appropriate membranes. However, a variety of characteristics of the mitochondrial genome suggests a much greater degree of similarity to certain plasmid DNAs than to the primary bacterial genome. Plasmids like mtDNA are also covalently closed circular DNA molecules which replicate with some degree of independence of the main bacterial nucleoid.

The contour size (molecular circumference) of circular mitochondrial DNA molecules ($5-32\,\mu$m) is very similar to that of bacterial plasmids ($2.3-33\,\mu$m) and very much smaller than that of bacterial nucleoid genomes ($100-1500\,\mu$m) (Table 7). Both plasmids and mitochondrial DNA molecules tend to form oligomers, which may be either unicircular (monomers linked in a single covalent circle) or catenated (monomers joined together rather like links in a chain). Experimental evidence from

Table 7 DNA sizes of some plasmids, bacteria, mycoplasma and mitochondria.

Source of DNA	contour (μm)	Size of DNA no. of nucleotide pairs	relative molecular mass
Small plasmid (Col El)	2.3	6.9×10^3	4.6×10^6
Large plasmid (*E. coli* F factor)	30	9.0×10^4	6.0×10^7
Mycoplasma (prokaryote)	100	3.0×10^5	2.0×10^8
Bacterium – *E. coli*	1330	4.0×10^6	2.6×10^9
mtDNA – animals	5	1.5×10^4	10^7
mtDNA – *Saccharomyces cerevisiae* (yeast)	27	8.0×10^4	5.4×10^7
mtDNA – *Pisum* (pea)	32	9.6×10^4	6.4×10^7

several research laboratories indicates that (*i*) both plasmids and mitochondrial DNAs contain polyribonucleotide tracts interrupting the polydeoxyribonucleotide sequence; (*ii*) the replication of both plasmids and mitochondrial DNAs can be dissociated from the replication of the central genetic species either by mutation or by administration of inhibitors of protein synthesis; and (*iii*) some plasmids and all mitochondrial DNAs can be eliminated by treatment with either acriflavine or ethidium bromide or related drugs.

The machinery for expression of the information in mitochondrial DNA has a number of similarities to that of present-day prokaryotes as already pointed out. However, the extent of these similarities is somewhat limited. According to a number of investigators the DNA-dependent RNA polymerases from mitochondria (the enzyme systems involved in transcription of the genetic information) are composed of single subunits, molecular weights being of the order of 50 000 to 65 000. Eukaryotic nuclear RNA polymerases and bacterial RNA polymerases are different from this, but are similar to each other in being composed of several subunits with total molecular weights in the range of 400 000 to 500 000.

Mitochondrial messenger RNA also resembles messenger RNA of nuclear origin in that both carry at their 3' OH ends, sequences of polyriboadenylic acid residues (polyA) thought possibly to be involved in processing or transporting messenger RNA from the nucleus to the ribosomes (ATTARDI and OJALA, 1973). The polyadenylic acid residues are added to the RNA subsequent to transcription. Such a polyA tail is *not* found on bacterial messenger RNAs.

Despite similarities between prokaryotic and mitochondrial ribosomes in sensitivities to a number of inhibitors of protein synthesis, the physical and chemical properties of the different classes of ribosome are not strikingly similar (see Table 3). The sedimentation values (S values) for mitochondrial ribosomes, their subunits and constituent ribosomal RNA molecules show considerable variations compared with the fairly uniform values observed for those of nuclear origin or from bacteria. Furthermore, there is little evidence in animals of mitochondrial ribosomes of the 5 S ribosomal RNA that is always present in the large subunits of ribosomes of nuclear or bacterial origin, although there is evidence for its existence in certain plant mitochondria. It is possible that in animal mitochondria there is an equivalent species of RNA, but that this is slightly smaller and sediments with the 4 S transfer fraction. However, it is still possible that there is no equivalent RNA species at all in certain mitochondria. Ribosomal RNAs from mitochondria appear to undergo somewhat less post-transcriptional methylation (chemical modification) than those from bacteria or those ribosomal RNAs outside the mitochondria. Methylation is thought to play an important part in the assembly and operation of ribosomes.

The picture which emerges from these observations is one of mitochondria possessing a macromolecular-synthesizing system not strikingly similar to those from either bacteria or eukaryotic nuclei. Those similarities between the prokaryotic and mitochondrial systems which actually do exist do not necessarily require that the mitochondrion originated as an endosymbiont, as the protoeukaryote itself, being of prokaryotic stock would undoubtedly have a wealth or prokaryotic characteristics. If the mitochondrion had an evolutionary origin from within the protoeukaryote it would be most surprizing indeed if a number of prokaryotic features had not been retained during mitochondrial evolution.

The plasmid theory for mitochondrial origin, as stated by RAFF and MAHLER (1975), envisages that the protoeukaryote was an advanced aerobic cell, bigger than usual for a prokaryote. The increase in cell volume would have been accompanied by an increase in quantity of the total respiratory membrane surface, in order to accommodate the increased energy requirement of the cell. This could have been achieved initially by invagination of the limiting membrane of the bacterium to give membranous infolds. Subsequently, these invaginations may have become severed to yield intracellular vesicles (see Fig. 3–1). However, although the formation of internal vesicles would greatly increase the potential for respiratory ATP synthesis, there would be a consequent problem of incorporation into the respiratory membranes of those components of the ATP-synthesizing system which appear to require synthesis *in situ*. In present day mitochondria some of the protein

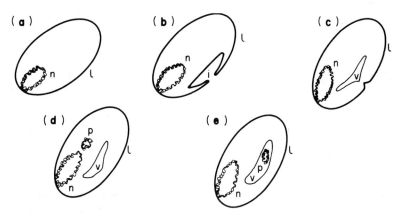

Fig. 3–1 The plasmid theory of mitochondrial origin. (**a**) Prokaryotic cell containing a nucleoid. (**b**) Invagination of prokaryotic limiting membranes. (**c**) Invagination leads to vesicle formation. (**d**) Excision of a plasmid from nucleoid DNA. (**e**) Incorporation of plasmid into vesicle giving DNA-containing mitochondrial evolutionary precursor. n, nucleoid; l, limiting membranes; i, invagination; v, vesicle; p, plasmid.

components of respiratory chain and of the ATP-synthesizing complex are coded and synthesized within the mitochondrion (see Table 2). Unless some mechanism evolved for synthesis of these components *in situ*, it would be necessary to replenish regularly the ATP-synthesizing vesicular system by further invaginations. Whilst such a system could hardly be considered efficient, the extra capacity for ATP synthesis provided by the vesicles could have outweighed this disadvantage. Increased efficiency could have been subsequently achieved by incorporation into a vesicle of a plasmid, originating from the nucleus (nucleoid) and containing the appropriate genes for synthesis of ribosomal RNAs, transfer RNAs and messenger RNAs for each protein species whose synthesis from within was essential.

Like the endosymbiont hypothesis this is also an attractive theory which cannot be ruled out. We would, in addition, suggest an alternative theory (REIJNDERS, 1975) which is really an extension of this one (Fig. 3–2). Under most conditions of growth, bacteria usually contain more than one copy of the genetic information. It is conceivable that a sufficiently large invagination of the limiting membrane could engulf one whole genome along with a portion of cytosolic fluid containing ribosomes, etc. Such an invagination would have to include the point of attachment of the DNA to the membrane which would facilitate further replication of the genome and subsequent division of the vesicle to produce multiple protomitochondria. As the DNA-containing vesicles

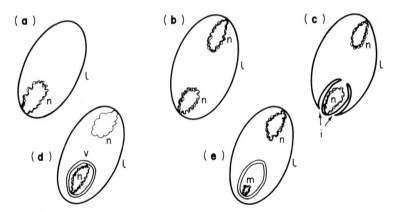

Fig. 3–2   Modified plasmid theory of mitochondrial origin. (**a**) Prokaryotic cell containing nucleoid. (**b**) Prokaryotic cell with duplicated nucleoid. (**c**) Cup-shaped invagination surrounds one of the nucleoids. (**d**) Invagination becomes a double membraned vesicle, surrounding a nucleoid attached to the inner membrane. (**e**) Loss of the nucleoid DNA within the vesicle leaving only those sequences concerned with ribosomal and transfer RNA and some of the components of the oxidative phosphorylation system. The vesicle is now a mitochondrial evolutionary precursor. n, nucleoid; l, limiting membranes; i, invagination; v, vesicle; m, 'mitochondrial' DNA.

became specialized for respiratory ATP synthesis there would be evolutionary pressure to eliminate those genes within the vesicle not directly concerned with providing a protein-synthesizing machinery and those respiratory components whose synthesis *in situ* is essential. It seems to us that this theory has the advantage over the plasmid theory in that it overcomes the difficulty of assembling all the necessary genes for rRNAs, tRNAs and respiratory components on a small plasmid when it is likely that the genes would be scattered on the bacterial genomes. Invagination at the point of DNA attachment also eases the problem of replicating the DNA when it arrives in the vesicle.

In some respects, this theory has similarities to the endosymbiont theory – in that the mitochondrion, in this case, begins its evolutionary history as an endosymbiont generated internally rather than from without.

3.3   Evolution of the nucleus, mitotic and meiotic cell division

It is perhaps surprizing that, in discussion of the origin of eukaryotic cells, so much attention has been paid to the mitochondria and chloroplasts and so little has been devoted to the most important of all organelles, the nucleus. A number of important differences between bacterial nucleoids and eukaryotic nuclei were listed in Table 7. Three major differences are restated here:

(*i*) In prokaryotes the genetic information is contained on only a single circular linkage group. The DNA is not associated with histone proteins. In eukaryotic cells, however, the genetic information is distributed amongst several individual chromosomes. The precise conformation of the DNA in eukaryotic chromosomes is not clear, as yet, but it is always associated with histone proteins.

(*ii*) The nucleoid DNA in prokaryotes is suspended in the cytosolic fluid in direct contact with the rest of the cellular components. In eukaryotes the chromosomes are surrounded by a double nuclear membrane which insulates them from the cytoplasmic constituents. Communication with the cytoplasm occurs by way of pores in the nuclear membrane.

(*iii*) Cell division in bacteria involves replication of the genetic material followed by a division of cell contents whereby a cell membrane and cell wall are formed between the two halves of the cell. Usually both daughters will receive a copy of the genetic information. In eukaryotes there is a much more complex process known as mitosis to separate precisely the duplicated chromosomes. This is necessitated by the subdivision of the genetic information into a number of chromosomes. In meiotic cell division, the situation is further complicated by the requirement that the chromosome number be reduced from the diploid to the haploid state and that a degree of 'shuffling' of genetic information take place (see KEMP, 1970).

It is relatively easy to see how a nuclear membrane could have arisen by mesosomal membranes enveloping the bacterial genome – in a similar way to that we have postulated for mitochondrial origin. It should be borne in mind, however, that the origin of the nuclear membrane would not be merely the simple physical event described above. It would be necessary to evolve the necessary genes for directing this process. It is possible that this might ensue from the evolution of an intracellular transporting system – a precursor of the endoplasmic reticulum, possibly essential for organization of cell processes in large cells. It would be a fairly simple matter to extend this system to provide a protective barrier to enclose the genetic complement of the cell. What is more difficult to envisage is how the complex process of mitosis arose.

Mitosis is a continuous process during which the duplicated chromosomes are split and separated to the two poles of the cell in a relatively precise manner by means of a spindle structure composed of microtubules. Division of the cytoplasm (cytokinesis) ensues, dividing also the two separate regions of genetic information – giving rise to two cells each indentical in genetic content with each other and their parent. For descriptive convenience the process is subdivided into six phases, shown in Fig. 3–3. It should be noted that in some primitive eukaryotes, the nuclear membrane does not break down during prophase and reform at the end of telophase.

Because of the central role of microtubules (§ 2.5) in mitosis and their universal presence in eukaryotes and absence from prokaryotes (except perhaps certain spirochaetes) it is believed that their acquisition was a crucial step in the evolution of eukaryotic cells. In some primitive eukaryotes, they seem to function only in mitosis and so it has been suggested that microtubules arose in the evolution of this process (see however, *Naegleria* – § 2.5). PICKETT-HEAPS (1974) has approached the problem of the evolution of mitosis by distinguishing two types of microtubular fibres in the spindle:

(*i*) those which run the length of the spindle from pole to pole (the continuous spindle), and

(*ii*) those which connect the chromosomal kinetochores of the centromeres to the poles.

The continuous spindle always seems to be present but some organisms lack the kinetochore to pole spindle fibres. During anaphase two types of microtubular activity often contribute to separation of kinetochores and their attached daughter chromosomes. Firstly, the continuous spindle fibres elongate – pushing the kinetochores apart and secondly, the kinetochore to pole spindle fibres usually (but not invariably) shorten, pulling the chromosomes in towards the poles.

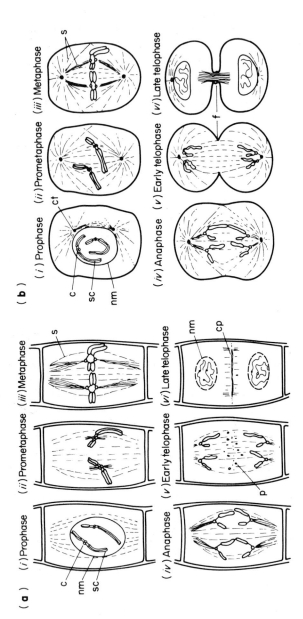

Fig. 3–3 (a) Mitotic spindles without centrioles, typical of most higher plant cells. **(b)** Mitotic spindles with centrioles as commonly seen in animal cells. c, centromere; ct, centriole; s, spindle filaments; f, furrowing of cell at cytokinesis (cleavage furrow); p, phragmoplast; cp, cell plate forms from phragmoplast. *Kinetochore is that part of the centromere which attaches to the spindle.

Pickett-Heaps believes that the former movement is relatively primitive and the latter a later development.

The starting point for the evolution of the mitotic process would have been the situation in which the genetic material had acquired a nuclear membrane possibly by the type of invaginations already mentioned. It is assumed that initially DNA would be attached to the newly evolved nuclear membrane. This situation would present something of a problem to an organism in ensuring that, at cell division, each daughter cell received a copy of the genetic material. This could have been achieved with a modicum of efficiency if there was some mechanism for elongation of the nucleus prior to cell division so that there would be a high probability that cytokinesis would lead to formation of daughter cells each acquiring a fully functional set of genetic information. The acquisition of microtubules making up a continuous spindle would clearly satisfy this need. Thus Pickett-Heaps suggests that, in the primitive nucleus, the genome was attached to a differentiated site on the nuclear membrane – the microtubule-organizing centre or MTOC for short. Mitosis would be achieved by replication of this site as the genomes replicated, the two daughter genomes being separated to opposite poles of the nucleus by the lengthening microtubules of the continuous spindle. Pickett-Heaps believes that some fungi may still, in fact, operate a primitive mitotic mechanism analogous to this one.

The next step in the evolution of the advanced spindle structure could have been that the point of attachment of the chromosomes to the nuclear membrane became a kinetochore, with its own MTOC, capable of forming a kinetochore to pole spindle. This could have been an important advantage if, at this stage, the genetic complement had started to subdivide into a number of chromosomes – each chromosome could thus have its own MTOC. The fact that a number of dinoflagellate species have chromosomes that remain attached to the nuclear membrane during mitosis, supports the idea that kinetochores arose from the nuclear membrane. In these species the nuclear membrane does not disintegrate at mitosis.

It is the view of Pickett-Heaps that centrioles arose by virtue of movement of the polar MTOC to the outside of the nuclear membrane. Evolution of the kinetochore would make the role of the polar MTOC in binding of chromosomes unnecessary. The polar MTOC could now play another important role in the generation of a cytoplasmic microtubular system. In some present day species the cytoplasmic MTOC is still associated with the nuclear membrane. The appearance of the centriole with its characteristic '9 + 0' structure of triplet microtubules would represent a sophistication and development of the polar MTOC as would the basal bodies of flagella and cilia. This suggestion is consistent with the observation that red algae, considered to be, perhaps, one of the

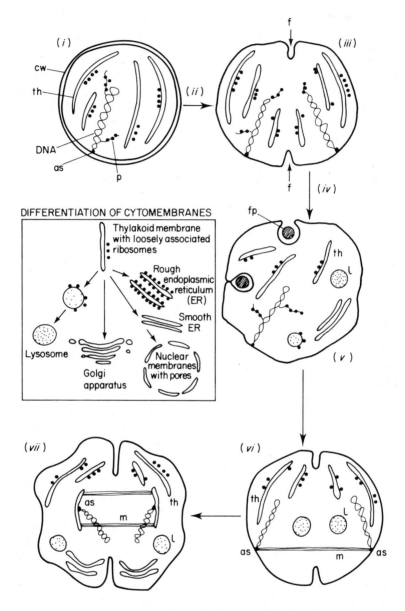

Fig. 3–4 The Cavalier-Smith hypothesis accounting for the origin of the eukaryote nucleus, mitosis and other eukaryote organelles. CW, cell wall; Th, thylakoid; AS, attachment site of DNA on membrane; P, polyribosome; F, cleavage furrow; FP, food particle; L, lysosome; M, microtubules. After CAVALIER-SMITH (1975) *Nature Lond.*, **256**, 463–8.

most primitive groups of eukaryotes, lack centrioles and flagella, although it is possible that the red algae have lost these organelles as a secondary feature.

One problem in understanding the evolution of eukaryotic cells is why do fairly advanced eukaryotes break down their nuclear membrane during mitosis? The ensuing mixture of nucleoplasm and cytoplasm must present some difficulties in segregating the various components or reformation of the nuclear membrane. This has presumably been offset partly by the ready supply of ATP necessary for the mechanical and biosynthetic processes of cell division which would be provided by movement of mitochondria into the nucleoplasm, and partly by the increased supply of tubulin available from the cytoplasm for spindle formation.

CAVALIER-SMITH (1975) has also considered the origin of mitosis and suggests that the evolution of phagocytosis was a critical event in the evolution of eukaryotic cells – setting up selection pressures which resulted not only in mitosis but also in the kind of physical compartmentation of the cell seen in present day eukaryotes (Fig. 3–4 inset). He suggests (Fig. 3–4(i)) that the protoeukaryote was a relatively large facultative prototrophic blue-green bacterium, with oxygenic photosynthesis and oxygen-utilizing ATP phosphorylation. The primary step would be the loss of the cell wall (Fig. 3–4(ii)) – an event which would explain the total absence of the prokaryotic peptido-glycan type of cell wall from all eukaryotes. The next phase would be the evolution of exocytosis. This is the blebbing off of membrane vesicles containing quantities of intracellular fluid. This could have evolved to facilitate extracellular digestion, using exocytosis to deliver concentrated enzyme solution to foodstuffs. According to Cavalier-Smith, exocytosis must have preceded endocytosis (phagocytosis or pinocytosis) as the latter would have led to an accumulation of intracellular food vacuoles (phagosomes) unless there was a means of re-fusion fo the phagosomes with the plasma membrane, i.e. exocytosis. Whether or not this is true, the processes are mechanistically so similar that it is likely that the evolution of one of these would rapidly lead to the evolution of the other. Clearly, in a situation where all other organisms are dependent upon absorption of predigested foodstuffs, the ability to engulf food particles by phagocytosis would have an enormous selective value. Furthermore this comparatively efficient heterotrophic way of life would have been an option available to the organism in dark or limited light conditions, whereas in sunlight it could switch to an autotrophic existence by photosynthesizing. Cavalier-Smith suggests that the molecular basis for exo- and endocytosis was a calcium-activated contractile actin–myosin-like microfilament system previously developed to achieve cleavage of the cell wall-less protoeukaryote by furrowing of the equatorial region of the cell membrane (Fig. 3–4 (iii and iv)). Attention is drawn to the similarities of the processes, each involving invagination, breakage and releasing of membranes. The differences seem to be ones of location and control rather than mechanism. The endocytotic theory suggests that mitosis arose because the highly mobile cell membrane would interfere with normal processes of chromosome segregation, the consequences of endo- or exocytotic elimination of the attachment point for the DNA being particularly serious. This implied the evolution of some new, non-membrane rigid segregation mechanism. Like Pickett-Heaps, Cavalier-Smith believes that the appearance of a microtubule system at this time was crucial. Initially, microtubules would have joined the two membrane attachment sites and pushed them apart, ensuring that a copy of the chromosome would end up on either side of the division furrow when it appeared (Fig. 3–4 (v)). This mechanism of chromosome separation would not now need to remain attached to the cell membrane but could now undergo endocytosis, taking the membrane attachment site plus a vesicle of attached membrane, possibly a forerunner of a nuclear membrane, into the interior of the cell (Fig. 3–4 (vi and vii)). The consequent development of an organelle specifically involved in harbouring the genetic information would permit the development of a more sophisticated and reliable method of chromosome segregation including the separation of the genome into a number of information units (chromosomes) which would be less liable to physical damage than a single large chromosome. These changes could not have occurred if the mechanism for ensuring chromosome segregation had remained attached to the cell membrane.

The theories of Pickett-Heaps and Cavalier-Smith are in no way contradictory. In fact, they are largely complementary, addressing themselves to different aspects of nuclear evolution. Cavalier-Smith extends his hypothesis to explain the origins of sexuality in eukaryotes. Clearly cytosis provided a mechanism for cell fusion. It is suggested that the initial selective advantage for cell fusion would have come at a time of starvation when food supplies would be shared – a total merger, rather than the structurally independent type of association usually encountered in symbioses. It is really very difficult to predict the advantages of sharing in terms of total food supply but a differential ability to make certain substances essential for growth could certainly have encouraged fusion at times when external food sources were poor. The large increase in genetic material in the fused cell would tend to be a burden on the biosynthetic machinery of the cell – particularly as much of the information would be redundant. Loss of chromosomes in a somewhat haphazard way that usually ensues on fusion of cells of different species would not be a terribly efficient process and there would be a considerable selective advantage to any diploid cell that was able to adapt its mitotic process to carry out a reduction division, i.e. meiosis. The necessity for exchange of genetic information in order to preserve the best features of both parents would lead to the recombination processes characteristic of meiosis (see Chapter 4).

The growth in size and complexity of the cell would have presented problems in terms of mobilization of metabolites from their site of synthesis to their site of use and of dilution of cell contents. Thus, there would have been a selective pressure to compartment the cellular contents. This could have been achieved by endocytosis and elaboration of the resulting internal membrane vesicles to give different types of endoplasmic reticulum, lysosomes, Golgi complex, etc. Cavalier-Smith also favours the proposal of RAFF and MAHLER (1975) that plasmids sequestered in suitable vesicles would have been the forerunners of chloroplast and mitochondrial DNA. Thus, the development of cytosis not only provided the evolutionary pressure for the development. of organelles – in terms of increased size and complexity, but also the where-with-all for their origin from endocytotic vesicles.

The theories for nuclear origin clearly merge well with the theory proposed by Raff and Mahler (1972, 1975) for mitochondrial origin. However, although they do prescribe a possible sequence for nuclear evolution, they do not preclude a parallel evolution of other organelles by an endosymbiotic process. It is clear that there is still much to be learned about these evolutionary processes. A detailed study of mitotic processes in a wide range of lower eukaryotes could be instructive, particularly if carried out in parallel with a range of biochemical studies. The most precise information will undoubtedly emerge, in time, from comparative studies on the amino acid sequences of some of the nuclear proteins, e.g. spindle tubulin, RNA polymerases, etc.

The attractions of the Cavalier-Smith hypothesis are three-fold.

(*i*) It explains how eukaryote nuclei evolved, thereby providing a plausible selective advantage for the evolution of most of the features of the typical nucleus, with the exception of histones. The evolution of histones in eukaryotes is, however, difficult to explain by any of the major theories. It seems likely that histones evolved to assist the efficient packing of DNA in meiotic pairing and segregation. Histones are absent in dinoflagellates, but sexual reproduction is also unknown in these organisms.

(*ii*) It gives plausible reasons for the differences between the genetic systems of the prokaryotes/chloroplasts/mitochondrial type and the nucleocytoplasmic system. As Cavalier-Smith comments . . . 'the symbiotic theories . . . ignore the fact that both kinds of genetic systems must have evolved from prokaryote systems and so resemblances are not at all surprizing. The real problem is why the nucleus is different, which endosymbiosis does not explain.'

(*iii*) It is much simpler than the symbiotic theory which postulates between two to five symbiotic events.

In essence, Cavalier-Smith proposes that the transition from prokaryote to eukaryote occurred in a line of photosynthetic organisms by a gradual series of evolutionary steps rather than an endosymbiotic 'jump'.

4 Summary and Conclusions

4.1 Was oxygen-detoxification responsible for initial endosymbiosis?

Although the serial endosymbiotic theory has received more extensive discussion in this book than any of the other theories, this does not necessarily imply that the S.E.T. is the most likely explanation but rather that the proponents of this hypothesis have been more active over the years. Even opponents of the S.E.T. would agree that Margulis's (1970) contribution has been to stimulate research workers to offer reasonable alternative explanations for the origin of eukaryotic cells from common as well as new evidence. All of the theories proposed, however, are based on one or other of two fundamentally different mechanisms of evolution. Firstly, there are those who propose that the eukaryotes evolved from prokaryotes by the progressive accumulation of advantageous mutations. On the other hand, the alternative theories are based on the essentially non-Mendelian mechanism of endosymbiosis. The endosymbiotic mechanism is likely to have given rise to a more rapid rate of evolution and explains the apparent discontinuity between the prokaryotes and eukaryotes. It also answers the criticism that there was insufficient time available for the eukaryotes to have evolved through the accumulation of mutations.

Since the S.E.T. is the most revolutionary of the two mechanisms proposed, it has had to answer to a greater number of criticisms. One of the major criticisms is that the protoeukaryote, being devoid of an aerobic respiratory pathway, would not have been able to compete successfully with the aerobic bacteria. This argument makes the assumption that the protoeukaryote was a strict anaerobe. This is doubtful. As we mentioned earlier (§ 1.4.2) oxygen-detoxification mechanisms probably existed long before aerobic respiration or oxygenic photosynthesis pathways had evolved (see Fig. 1–7). Of course, the aerobic bacteria would have been energetically more successful than the oxygen-tolerant protoeukaryote. Even so, the two groups of organisms would not have been competing directly for the same resources since it was the non-motile aerobic bacterium that the phagocytic protoeukaryote would have preyed upon. Therefore, it seems likely that the protoeukaryote and others of its kind would have co-existed favourably with the aerobic bacteria.

Another problem with the S.E.T. is that it assumes that the initial bacterial invasion of the protoeukaryote gave rise to an endosymbiosis in which the host gave protection and nutrients to the endosymbiont in return for a more efficiently produced source of ATP from the endosymbiont. The fact that we know of few existing prokaryotes that possess an ADP/ATP carrier (transporter) suggests that the initial endosymbiosis was maintained for other reasons. We believe that the primary advantage to the host in the first place could have been *oxygen-detoxification*. For instance, aerobic respiration, being a more efficient means of oxygen-detoxification than those mentioned in § 1.4, might have provided the selective advantage needed to make the initial endosymbiosis successful. Although it seems unlikely that the prokaryotic endosymbiont provided its own carrier for moving ADP and ATP across its limiting membrane, we do know of one modern-day prokaryote, *Rickettsia prowazeki*, which does possess such a facility. Nevertheless, this organism probably evolved this carrier as an adaptation and not as a pre-requisite to its endoparasitic way of life. Likewise, the promitochondrion could have acquired its ADP/ATP carrier *after* the initial endosymbiosis had been established.

4.2 The integration of genetic systems and the problem of gene transfer

Implicit in the S.E.T. is the concept of gene transfer from the endosymbiont to the host nucleus. Until recently this had weakened the argument for the S.E.T. because no supportive evidence was available. However, we now know that gene transfer is possible from prokaryote to eukaryotic nucleus and that, for at least one mitochondrial protein, gene transfer from the mitochondrion to the nucleus has probably occurred during the course of evolution (see § 2.6).

Protagonists of the S.E.T. often fail to comment on the non-prokaryotic features of mitochondria and chloroplasts. For example, many eukaryotic genomes – including those of mitochondria and chloroplasts – have 'split genes', whilst those of bacteria do not. That is, eukaryotic genomes are often split so that the genetic material for a protein or RNA molecule is separated by stretches of DNA called *introns*, which are eventually removed from the RNA transcripts. It may be that introns play a part in the control of gene expression even though their precise function has not yet been determined. Since the assembly of mitochondria and chloroplasts is brought about through the cooperation of nuclear and organellar genomes, it is not surprising to find that there are similarities in gene structure and control mechanisms between the nucleus and cytoplasmic organelles. What is remarkable, however, is the discovery by MACINO *et al.* (1979) that the genetic code employed by yeast mitochondrial genes deviates from that of both prokaryote genes and eukaryotic nuclear genes. For example, the yeast mitochondrial codon for the amino acid, tryptophan, is UGA, which in prokaryotic and eukaryotic nuclear systems does not code for any of the amino acids but, instead, signals the end of a gene. This finding has now been confirmed for other mitochondria including those from humans, though introns appear to be absent in human mtDNA. Mitochondria therefore, have deviated from the universal code! Furthermore, mitochondria use fewer tRNA species by having a simpler decoding strategy than other genetic systems. These are yet further examples of the extent to which the nuclear and organellar genetic systems have diverged from each other and from those of prokaryotes during the last 1.5×10^9 years:

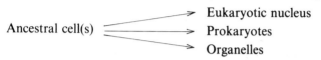

At first sight, this might seem to be a contradictory state of affairs because in some respects we find that the mitochondrial and nuclear genetic systems are very different and yet, in other ways, they show similarities. However, this is essentially what evolution is all about. It *conserves* those features that are useful and, at the same time, it can permit *divergence* as conditions change.

Thus we can explain the differences and similarities between organelles, prokaryotes, and eukaryotic nuclear systems both in terms of diversification and conservation, this being consistent with either of the proposed mechanisms for the origin of eukaryotic cells.

4.3   Eukaryote phylogeny and meiosis

One of the problems that the S.E.T. *specifically* seeks to explain is the discontinuity in the fossil record between the prokaryotes and eukaryotes. But it is questionable as to whether a fossil discontinuity really does exist because microfossils are very difficult to analyse and often impossible to classify as eukaryotic or prokaryotic. Therefore, we must resort to constructing an evolutionary scheme based on the study of contemporary organisms. It is possible to do this by an analysis of biochemical pathways, intracellular organization, and gross morphological features. This is the systematic approach to the problem. One of the most useful of modern tools for studying phylogeny, however, is to look at the genetic record found in the sequences of homologous proteins and RNA molecules. SCHWARTZ and DAYHOFF (1978) have constructed a composite evolutionary tree based on sequence data from ferredoxins, c-type cytochromes, and 5S rRNA molecules from several species (Fig. 4–1). Two important conclusions can be drawn from this study. Firstly, the data suggests that aerobic respiration preceded oxygenic photosynthesis. This implies that the *initial* increase in atmospheric oxygen was by photodissociation, a finding consistent with the idea that efficient mechanisms for coping with oxygen-detoxification (i.e. respiration) would have been required before oxygen-releasing

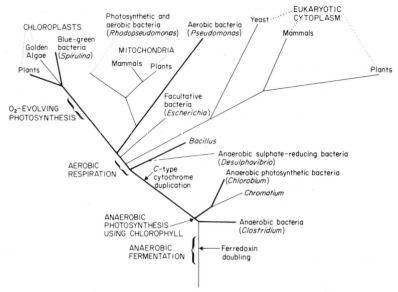

Fig. 4–1 The composite tree represents an evolutionary scheme based on amino acid and nucleotide sequence data for the *c*-type cytochromes, ferredoxins and 5 S ribosomal RNAs. The tree represents the only *quantitative* attempt to construct phylogenies, since branches are drawn proportional to the amount of evolutionary change that they represent. Bold lines are calculated from a matrix of evolutionary distances based upon the combination of two or more different trees; thin lines are derived from a single tree. The idea is that many proteins and nucleic acids are 'living fossils' in so far as their structures have been dynamically conserved by the evolutionary process over thousands of millions of years. Evolutionary tree distances are therefore based upon units of accepted point mutations per 100 residues (amino acids). (Redrawn after Schwartz and Dayhoff, 1978, *Science*, N. Y., **199**, 400.)

photosynthesis could have evolved. The tree also shows that, at the time when the aerobic bacteria emerged, the eukaryotic line was diverging, thus supporting the proposal that the protoeukaryote was a facultative aerobe. The idea that photosynthetic and respiratory electron transport systems had a common origin (§ 1.4) is supported by the finding that mitochondria appear to share a recent ancestry with photosynthetic bacteria as well as with aerobic bacteria. Lastly, the grouping together of chloroplasts, mitochondria and present-day prokaryotes is compatible with the endosymbiotic theory for the origin of eukaryotes. Indeed, *if* the composite tree does represent an accurate picture of molecular evolution, then suggestions by opponents of S. E. T. that the mitochondrial and chloroplast genomes were derived in some way from the nuclear genome, which then underwent rapid divergence, seem unlikely

for the following reasons. Since cytochrome-*c* sequence analyses
indicate a purple non-sulphur bacterial origin (*Rhodopseudomonas*) for
the origin of mitochondria, then opponents of S.E.T. must postulate a
purple non-sulphur bacterial origin for the *whole* eukaryotic cell, with
rapid divergence of the nuclear genome, together with the rRNA that it
encodes. On the other hand, the very close relationship between
chloroplasts and blue-green bacteria would argue a blue-green bacterial
origin for the *whole* eukaryotic cell, with again rapid evolutionary
divergence of the nuclear genome etc. Both postulates cannot be correct,
unless an intermediate between a blue-green and a purple non-sulphur
bacterium is proposed. Data from the composite tree, however, show
that blue-green bacteria and purple non-sulphur bacteria diverged long
before chloroplasts and blue-green bacteria on the one hand, or
mitochondria and purple non-sulphur bacteria on the other.
Unfortunately, we cannot be certain that the tree is an accurate
representation of phylogeny. Caution should be adopted because
constructing evolutionary trees of this sort requires that many assump-
tions be made.

It is to the primitive protists that we look to find further clues to the
problem of eukaryotic origins. A careful study of their modes of
nutrition, reproduction, and locomotion might make it possible to
ascertain which group represents the most primitive eukaryotic form.
The rhodophytes are generally regarded as one of the most primitive
groups of nucleate organisms because they share more common features
with the blue-green bacteria than any other group of eukaryotes. For
example, they show similarities in photosynthetic pigments, thylakoid
lamellae and, in addition, both groups lack flagella. This is what we
should expect if the rhodophytes are directly descended from blue-green
bacteria. Of course, the alternative explanation is that the rhodophytes
evolved through endosymbiosis between an amoeboid organism and a
blue-green bacterium. In this case, we should regard the amoebae as
representing the most primitive group of eukaryotic organisms, a
proposal consistent with the observation that amoebo-flagellates are
more primitive with respect to their mode of reproduction than
rhodophytes. For example, the amoebo-flagellates are not known to be
sexual and some species even lack conventional mitosis. By contrast,
most rhodophytes reproduce sexually and possess a well-developed
spindle. So, do rhodophytes or amoebo-flagellates represent the most
primitive group?

If Cavalier-Smith's views are correct (§ 3.3) then eukaryotes evolved
from prokaryotes via a sexual non-flagellate amoeboid alga (almost a
'rhodophyte'!) and that amoebo-flagellates evolved later. The main
objection to this is firstly the virtual absence of sexual reproduction from
non-flagellate amoeboid organisms, so that a transitional organism of
the kind proposed by Cavalier-Smith is unlikely. Secondly, it is

necessary to propose that a highly conserved feature such as sexuality was lost in the evolution leading to amoeba-flagellates. By contrast, Margulis (1970)proposes that the amoebo-flagellate condition is more primitive since the protoeukaryote (amoeboid) acquired a primitive flagellum by endosymbiosis (§ 2.5) and that the mitotic spindle in turn evolved from the flagellum. Furthermore, in the development of the spindle from the primitive flagellum, Margulis argues that the flagellum apparatus was taken over completely and subsequently a secondary flagellum developed from a genetically duplicated mitotic centre. Margulis therefore postulates the *spindle* as the key feature of the mitotic system thus giving rise to an evolutionary sequence, which was first outlined in § 2.5: amoeba $\longrightarrow$ amitotic flagellate (or amoebo-flagellate) $\longrightarrow$ mitotic amoeba $\longrightarrow$ mitotic flagellate. PICKETT-HEAPS (1974), however, takes the opposite view, namely that *chromosomes* are the essential features of mitosis and that the spindle system evolved *before* the flagellum and that subsequently the flagellum developed from the spindle and not through endosymbiosis. Pickett-Heaps also proposes that the mitotic apparatus arose first in algae. However, as we have stated above, there are objections to this last point, and it seems just as likely that the mitotic apparatus arose first in protozoa. The 'compromise' idea that the mitotic apparatus first appeared in protozoa and that the flagellum subsequently evolved from the mitotic system, is one that is favoured by McQUADE (1977). He proposes that eukaryotes evolved through the successive stages – amoeba, flagellate, sexual flagellate – and that sexuality emerged only once. He adopts this view after close examination of the two forms of flagella that are found in living organisms, namely 'whiplash' (simple form) and 'tinsel' (complex form). Because certain amoebo-flagellates possess *two* whiplash flagella, the original flagellate is depicted with this form. Moreover, if flagella arose from the two mitotic centres, then a paired form would be expected, which is supported by the observation that the basal bodies to the flagella in the amoebo-flagellate, *Naegleria* (§ 2.5) appear to function as mitotic centres. The development later of tinsel-form flagella alongside whip-like flagella are characteristic of certain 'lower' sexual eukaryotes and McQuade therefore proposes ' . . . that sexuality arose in a line of organisms possessing, or capable of producing, both types of flagellum'. The absence of flagella in rhodophytes is seen as a secondary loss.

The evolution of meiotic cell division and sexual reproduction is one of the most important developments in eukaryotes. Another extremely important development was the evolution of histone proteins associated with DNA – a most distinctive feature of eukaryotes. Indeed, the evolution of histone proteins may well have been the first major step in the development of nucleate (eukaryote) organisms. So evolution of multiple, linear chromosomes (comprising DNA + histone) and a

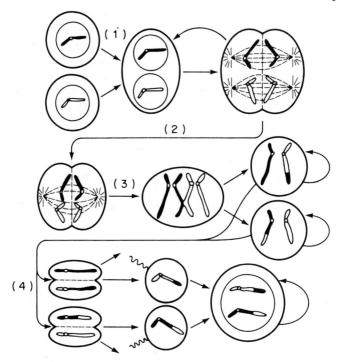

Fig. 4–2 A scheme for the origin of sex. (1) Fusion of haploid cells to form a heterokaryon (i.e. a cell with more than one nucleus of different genetic constitution). (2) Origin of diploid from heterokaryon. (3) Chiasma formation during mitosis ('somatic crossing over') generates variability within a clone. (4) Reduction and syngamy restores heterozygosity. (Reproduced from Maynard Smith, 1978, *Evolution of Sex*. Cambridge University Press.)

spindle structure typical of mitosis, was the first step in meiotic evolution. How meiosis actually evolved in essentially asexual organisms is debateable, but a plausible scheme has been proposed by MAYNARD-SMITH (1978) (Fig.4–2).

Eukaryotic sex is a mechanism that recombines characteristics so as to generate more genetic variability than could be accomplished by the accumulation of mutations in asexual species. Interestingly, endosymbiosis is analogous to sex in that it combines genetic characters but from two *unrelated* species. Indeed, before eukaryotic sex had evolved, endosymbiosis may have been a successful feature in the advancement of evolution.

4.4 How many kingdoms of organisms are there?

To conclude, an improved understanding of the evolutionary origins of eukaryotes should help biologists to construct more natural schemes of classification. In this respect, the techniques of sequencing and oligonucleotide cataloguing are of particular value in providing a truly quantitative basis for determining phylogenetic relationships between contemporary groups of organisms. Most biologists accept that a discontinuity exists between the prokaryotes and eukaryotes and the taxonomists incorporate this as a boundary in their schemes of classification. At present, WHITTAKER's (1969) five kingdom system (Monera, Protista, Plantae, Animalia, and Fungi) seems to be a very acceptable scheme of classification (Fig. 4–3). Unfortunately, by grouping the protists into one kingdom, Whittaker's system fails to recognize the protists as forerunners of plants, animals and fungi. Sequencing data might help resolve this problem, but in the meantime LEEDALE's (1974) alternative proposal (Fig. 4–4) goes part way to meeting the objection in the Whittaker scheme. Here, the Protista are

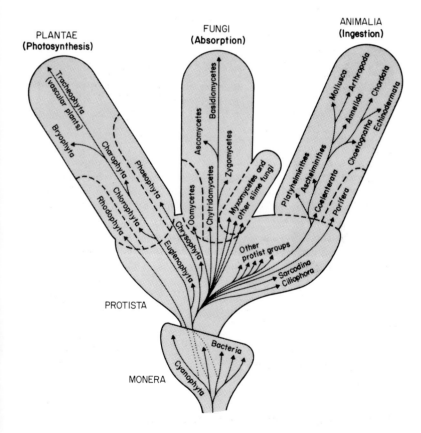

Fig. 4–3 Whittaker's five-kingdom scheme. (Adapted from Whittaker, R. H., 1969, *Science, N. Y.*, **163**, 150–9.)

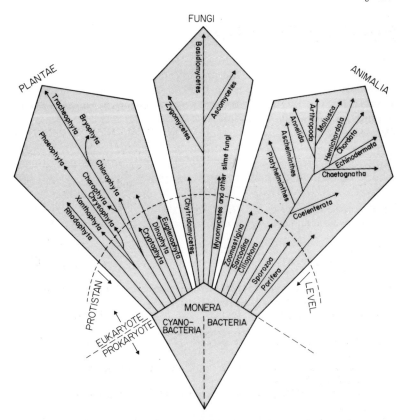

Fig. 4–4 Leedale's four-kingdom scheme in which the Protista do not appear as a kingdom. It does however, emphasize the discontinuity between prokaryotes and eukaryotes.* Several groups within the protistan level, included in Leedale's original scheme, are not shown here. (Adapted after Leedale, G. F., 1974, *Taxon*, **23**, 261–70.)

dispersed and absorbed into the higher kingdoms, thus getting round the placement of such difficult phyla as the Chlorophyta, and yet acknowledging the 'protistan level' within the scheme. Nevertheless, as Leedale acknowledges, even this scheme has its drawbacks, but like the serial endosymbiotic theory or the alternative theories that have been presented to account for the evolution of eukaryotes, it should provide a model for discussion, which, as new evidence comes to light, will require modification.

Further Reading

ATTARDI, G. and OJALA, D. (1974). In *The Biogenesis of Mitochondria*, Kroon and Saccone (Eds). Academic Press.

BONEN, L. and DOOLITTLE, W. F. (1975). On the prokaryotic nature of red algal chloroplasts. *Proc. Natl. Acad. Sci. (U.S.A)*, **72**, 2310–14.

BORST, P. and GRIVELL, L. A. (1978). The mitochondrial genome of yeast. *Cell*, **15**, 705–23.

CAVALIER-SMITH, T. (1975). The origin of núclei and of eukaryotic cells. *Nature, Lond.*, **256**, 463–8.

DICKERSON, R. E., TIMKOVICH, R. and ALMASSY, R. J. (1976). The cytochrome fold and the evolution of bacterial energy metabolism. *J. molec. Biol.*, **100**, 473–91.

DICKERSON, R. E. (1978). Chemical evolution and the origin of life. *Scientific American*, **239**, 62–78. [One of nine papers in this volume given over entirely to 'Evolution'.]

HALL, D. O. and RAO, K. K. (1981) *Photosynthesis*, 3rd edition. Studies in Biology, no. 37. Edward Arnold, London.

HINNEN, A., HICKS, J. B. and FINK, G. R. (1978), Transformation of yeast. *Proc. Natl. Acad. Sci.*, **75**(4), 1929–33.

KEMP, R. (1970). *Cell Division and Heredity*, Studies in Biology, no. 21. Edward Arnold, London.

JEONS, K. W. and JEONS, M. S. (1976). Endosymbiosis in amoebae. *J. Cell Physiol.*, **89**, 337–44.

LEEDALE, G. F. (1974). How many are the kingdoms of organisms? *Taxon*, **23**, 261–70.

LOCKWOOD, A. P. M. (1979). *The Membranes of Animal Cells*, 2nd edition. Studies in Biology, no. 27. Edward Arnold, London.

LEWIN, R. A. (1976). Prochlorophyta as a proposed new division of algae. *Nature, Lond.*, **261**, 697–8.

McQUADE, A. B. (1977). Origins of the nucleate organisms. *Quart. Rev. Biol.*, **52**, 249–62.

MACINO, G., CORRUZI, G., NOBREGA, F. G., LI, M. and TZAGALOFF, A. (1979). Use of the UGA terminator as a tryptophan codon in yeast mitochondria. *Proc. Natl. Acad. Sci.* (U.S.A.), **76**, 3784–5. [Article summarized in *New Scientist*, **84**, 439 (1979).]

MARGULIS, L. (1970). *Origin of Eukaryotic Cells*. Yale University Press.

MARGULIS, L., TO, L. and CHASE, D. (1978). Microtubules in prokaryotes. *Science, N. Y.*, **200**, 1118–24. [See also *Proc. Roy. Soc. Lond. B*, **204**.]

MAYNARD-SMITH, J. (1978). *The Evolution of Sex*. Cambridge University Press, Cambridge.

MUSCATINE, L. and POOL, R. R. (1979). Regulation of numbers of intracellular algae. *Proc. Roy. Soc. Lond. B*, **204**, 131–39.

PECHMAN, K. J. and WOESE, C. R. (1972). Characterization of the primary structural homology between the 16S ribosomal RNAs of *Escherichia coli* and *Bacillus megaterium* by oligomer cataloguing. *J. Molec. Evol.*, **1**, 230–40.

PICKETT-HEAPS, J. D. (1974). The evolution of mitosis and the eukaryotic conditions. *Biosystems*, **6**, 37–48.

PREER, J. R., PREER, J. V. and JURAND, A. (1974). Kappa and other endosymbionts in *Paramecium aurelia*. *Bact. Rev.*, **38**, 113–63.

RAFF, R. A. and MAHLER, H. R. (1972). The non-symbiotic origin of mitochondria. *Science, N. Y.* **171**, 575–82.

RAFF, R. A. and MAHLER, H. R. (1975). The symbiont that never was: an enquiry into the evolutionary origin of the mitochondrion. In *Symbiosis*, pp. 41–92. S.E.B. Symposium No. XXIV. Cambridge University Press. [This volume contains other papers concerned with the origin of eukaryotic cells.]

RAVEN, P. H. (1970). A multiple origin for plastids and mitochondria. *Science, N. Y.*, **169**, 641–6.

REIJNDERS, L. (1975). The origin of mitochondria. *J. molec. Evol.*, **5**, 167–76.

SCHOPF, J. W. (1978). The evolution of the earliest cells. *Scientific American*, **239**, 110–38.

SCHWARTZ, R. M. and DAYHOFF, M. O. (1978). Origins of prokaryotes, eukaryotes, mitochondria and chloroplasts. *Science, N. Y.*, **199**, 395–403.

SCOTT, G. D. (1969). *Plant Symbiosis*, Studies in Biology, no. 16. Edward Arnold, London.

SMITH, D. C. (1979). From extracellular to intracellular: the establishment of a symbiosis. *Proc. Roy. Soc. Land. B*, **204**, 115–30. [One of eleven papers included in this volume under the title *The Cell as a Habitat*. A discussion organized by M. H. Richmond and D. C. Smith, F.R.S.]

STANIER, R. J. (1970). Some aspects of the biology of cells and their possible evolutionary significance. *Symp. Soc. gen. Mircobiol.*, **20**, 1–38.

TAYLOR, F. J. R. (1974). Implications and extensions of the serial endosymbiotic theory of the origin of eukaryotes. *Taxon*, **23**, 229–58.

TAYLOR, F. J. R. (1979). Symbioticism revisited: a discussion of the evolutionary impact of intracellular symbioses. *Proc. Roy. Soc. Lond. B*, **204**, 267–86.

TRIBE, M. A. and WHITTAKER, P. A. (1981) – *Chloroplasts and Mitochondria*, 2nd edition. Studies in Biology, no. 31. Edward Arnold, London.

WHATLEY, J. M. (1976). Bacteria and nuclei in *Pelomyxa palustris*: comments on the theory of serial endosymbiosis. *New Phytol.*, **76**, 111–18.

WHATLEY, J. M., JOHN, P. and WHATLEY, F. R. (1979). From extracellular to intracellular: the establishment of mitochondria and chloroplasts. *Proc. Roy. Soc. Lond. B*, **204**, 165–87.

WHITTAKER, R. H. (1969). New concepts of kingdoms of organisms. *Science, N. Y.*, **163**, 150–9.

WOESE, C. R. and FOX, G. E. (1977). The concept of cellular evolution. *J. Molec. Evol.*, **10**, 1–6.